Contents

Chapter activities

Chapter activities – answers

Practice assessments

Practice assessments – answers

Acknowledgements

The publisher wishes to thank the following for their help with the reading and production of the book: Hania Lee, Maz Loton, Jon Moore, Cathy Turner and Jean Cox. Thanks are also due to Roger Petheram for his technical editorial work and to Laura Ingham for her designs for this series.

The publisher is indebted to the Association of Accounting Technicians for its help and advice to our authors and editors during the preparation of this text.

Authors

David Cox has more than twenty years' experience teaching accountancy students over a wide range of levels. Formerly with the Management and Professional Studies Department at Worcester College of Technology, he now lectures on a freelance basis and carries out educational consultancy work in accountancy studies. He is author and joint author of a number of textbooks in the areas of accounting, finance and banking.

Michael Fardon has extensive teaching experience of a wide range of banking, business and accountancy courses at Worcester College of Technology. He now specialises in writing business and financial texts and is General Editor at Osborne Books. He is also an educational consultant and has worked extensively in the areas of vocational business curriculum development.

Basic accounting 2

Workbook

third edition

David Cox

Michael Fardon

osborne
BOOKS

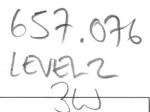

NEW AAT WISE GUIDES – for convenient exam revision

This handy pocket-sized guide provides the **perfect study and revision resource** for the AAT Level 2 Certificate in Accounting.

now available for:
Basic Accounting 1
Basic Accounting 2
Basic Costing

Visit www.osbornebooks.co.uk to **view free sample material** and place your order.

© David Cox, Michael Fardon, 2010, second edition 2011, third edition 2012.

Published by Osborne Books Limited
Unit 1B Everoak Estate
Bromyard Road
Worcester WR2 5HP
Tel 01905 748071
Email books@osbornebooks.co.uk
Website www.osbornebooks.co.uk

Design by Laura Ingham
Cover and page design image © Istockphoto.com/Petrovich9

Printed and bound by CPI Group (UK) Ltd, Croydon, CR0 4YY

British Library Cataloguing in Publication Data
A catalogue record for this book is available from the British Library

ISBN 978 1905777 730

Introduction

what this book contains

This book has been written specifically to cover Learning Area 'Basic Accounting II' which combines five QCF Units in the AAT Level 2 Certificate in Accounting:

- Maintaining and reconciling the cash book
- Banking procedures
- Maintaining petty cash records
- Maintaining the journal
- Maintaining control accounts

This book is set out in two sections:

- **Chapter activities** which provide extra practice material in addition to the activities included in the Osborne Books Tutorial text. Answers to the Chapter activities are set out in this book.

- **Practice assessments** are included to prepare the student for the Computer Based Assessments. They are based directly on the structure, style and content of the sample assessment material provided by the AAT at www.aat.org.uk. Suggested answers to the Practice assessments are set out in this book.

online support from Osborne Books

This book is supported by practice material available at www.osbornebooks.co.uk

This material is available to tutors – and to students at their discretion – in two forms:

- A **Tutor Zone** which is available to tutors who have adopted the Osborne Books texts. This area of the website provides extra assessment practice material (plus answers) in addition to the activities included in this Workbook text.

- **Online learning** – online practice questions designed to familiarise students with the style of the AAT Computer Based Assessments.

    Scan the code on the right using your Smartphone to gain access to the online practice questions.

further information

If you want to know more about our products, please visit www.osbornebooks.co.uk, email books@osbornebooks.co.uk or telephone Osborne Books Customer Services on 01905 748071.

Chapter activities

Chapter activities
1
Introduction to banking procedures

1.1 Banks and building societies offer many similar services.

From the list below tick the services that are offered by banks and/or building societies.

Service	Offered by banks	Offered by building societies
Debit card		
Business current account		
Personal current account		
House mortgage		
Safe custody		
Savings accounts		
Investments		
Insurance		
Personal loan		

1.2 When a customer pays in a cheque to a bank, the customer is safe to withdraw the amount of that cheque after

	✔
2 working days	
4 working days	
6 working days	

Select the correct option.

1.3   Banking documents should normally be retained for a period of at least . . .

	✔
one year	
six years	
eight years	

Select the correct option

1.4   A dishonoured cheque is . . .

	✔
a cheque that has been refused by the person to whom it is made payable	
a cheque that a customer has issued but the bank refuses to pay	
a cheque that a customer has refused to issue because the goods supplied are faulty	

Select the correct option

1.5   A prepayment card is . . .

	✔
a card which can be purchased by a customer and has an amount programmed in which the customer can use up by making purchases	
a card issued to a customer which enables the customer to make purchases and pay for them later	
a card only issued to customers over 18 which enables them to make purchases overseas	

Select the correct option

Chapter activities

2 Receiving and recording payments

2.1 A business receiving cash for sales that it has made operates a cash till.

At the end of each working day the cash in the till is counted and a certain amount is kept in the till as a 'float' and the rest paid into the bank on paying-in slip.

On Monday the cashier noted the following details:

	£	£
Cash float in the till at the beginning of the day		275.00
Cash receipts from sales during the day:	25.00	
	19.65	
	76.40	
	32.50	
	67.95	
	125.90	
	4.50	
Cash taken from the cash till for paying in at the bank		380.90

Answer the following questions:

(a) What was the total of the cash received during the day?

(b) What was the total of the cash in the till at the end of the day before the cash for paying in at the bank was taken out?

(c) What was the total of the cash float held overnight on Monday?

2.2   You work for Tandem Limited and deal with cheques received from customers. Part of your job is to check the cheques and either pass them forward for listing and paying in at the bank or query them.

During the course of Monday 20 October 20XX you receive a cheque which you think may cause a problem.

State two reasons why this cheque should not be paid into the bank.

(a)

(b)

2.3   'Chargeback' in relation to a card payment means that

	✔
the purchaser who receives faulty or incorrect goods bought using a debit or credit card can claim back the amount paid	
a business selling goods online is entitled to deduct postage and packing charges from the purchaser's account if a debit card is used	

Select the correct option

2.4 When an online trader accepts debit and credit card payments, the customer fills in an online order form and provides details, including

	✔
date of birth, card number, security code	
date of birth, card number, expiry date	
card number, expiry date, security code	

Which one of these options is correct?

2.5 A business receives a remittance advice (shown below) which is unfortunately incomplete.

TO	**REMITTANCE ADVICE**	FROM
Bristol Street Supplies 67 Bristol Street Bartfield BA6 7TY	2 December 20XX	**Helford Ltd** **16 Kent Road** **Manorfield** **MA2 6GP**

date	your reference	our reference	payment amount
03 11 XX	INVOICE 10956	3213	700.00
15 11 XX	INVOICE 11024	3287	325.95
20 11 XX	CREDIT NOTE 167	3287	(45.60)
		TOTAL	

(a) What should the total figure be?

(b) There are two common methods of sending money in settlement of accounts. They are:

(c) Which method is most likely to have been used in this case, bearing in mind the details shown on the remittance advice?

3 Chapter activities
Paying into the bank

3.1 The cheque shown below has to be paid into the bank.

There are a number of problems with the cheque.

Southern Bank PLC
Stourminster Branch
10 High Street, Stourminster ST1 8HJ

date _____   97-76-66

Pay   *J Hart Sports Ltd* _____   only

Two hundred pounds only   £ *210.00*

CAPELLO DESIGNS
R Capello

Account payee only

635105   977666   68381110   Director

What action would you need to take in the following circumstances:

(a) The amount in words and figures is different

(b) There is no date on the cheque

3.2 You work for Plumstead Traders Limited, which has a bank account at Central Bank, Persham. You are required to prepare the paying-in slip and counterfoil as at today's date. The cheques are to be listed and totalled on the back of the paying-in slip. The items to be banked are:

Cash

three £20 notes

six £10 notes

two £5 notes

four £1 coins

two 50p coins

four 10p coins

three 2p coins

Cheques

£60.00   Balkan Enterprises

£65.60   Mindwell Catering

£99.95   C Harrison & Co

£24.00   H Richter

Date _____		Date _____	**bank giro credit**		£50 notes		
Credit _____		Cashier's stamp and initials			£20 notes		
£50 notes			**Code no** 76-23-88		£10 notes		
£20 notes			**Bank** CENTRAL BANK		£5 notes		
£10 notes			**Branch** PERSHAM		£1 £2		
£5 notes					50p		
£1 £2		Credit _____	PLUMSTEAD TRADERS LTD		20p		
50p		Account No. 12097453			10p,5p		
20p					Bronze		
10p,5p					Total Cash		
Bronze		**Number of cheques**	Paid in by _____		Cheques etc		
Total Cash							
Cheques etc			Do not write below this line		£		
£		76-23-88 12097453 77					

Counterfoil		Cheques	
£		Carried over £	

3.3   You work for Butterworth Ltd, which has a bank account at Albion Bank, Broadfield. Butterworth Ltd has an online shop. You have just received the December bank statement, which is shown below. Study the statement and answer the questions that follow.

Albion Bank plc
7 The Avenue, Broadfield, BR1 2AJ

		Account title	Butterworth	
		Account number	15239524	
		Statement	15	

Date	Details	Payments	Receipts	Balance
20XX				
3 Dec	Balance brought down			1,750.00 CR
8 Dec	BACS Credit D Guest		3,430.00	5,180.00 CR
12 Dec	DD Wyvern Insurance	260.60		4,919.40 CR
12 Dec	526147	150.00		4,769.40 CR
14 Dec	526148	67.45		4,701.95 CR
15 Dec	Websales 24237942		2,960.00	7,661.95 CR
16 Dec	SO Granby Finance	680.00		6,981.95 CR
16 Dec	Giro Credit 92842		1,195.60	8,177.55 CR
22 Dec	BACS Payroll	4,127.00		4,050.55 CR
24 Dec	Bank Charges	490.70		3,559.85 CR

(a)   Explain how the payment received on 8 December is made to the bank.

(b)   Explain the payment received on 15 December.

(c)   If the payment into the bank received on 16 December had contained a cheque for £350 which was then dishonoured and sent back to Albion Bank, what would the balance of the bank account have been on 24 December?

4   Chapter activities
Making payments

4.1   A business will need to carry out a series of internal checks and procedures before making a payment to a supplier.

Indicate from the following list the checks and procedures that will normally be needed before a payment is made to a supplier. State 'yes' or 'no'.

Check or procedure	Yes ✔	No ✔
Documents (eg purchase order, delivery note, invoice) checked against each other to make sure they tie up	✔	
Any credit due has been acknowledged in the form of a credit note		✔
Any remittance advice due has been received		
Any discounts due have been allowed by the supplier		
All invoices have been given at least 30 days credit		✔
Payment authorisation has been given	✔	

4.2   A bank giro credit can be used in order to: ✔

make payment of a bill direct to a bank account	
advise a supplier that a payment has been sent to a bank account	
obtain cash from the bank to pay wages	

Select the correct option.

4.3   A BACS direct credit is normally used in order to:

	✔
pay bank charges	
make payments to suppliers	
pay insurance premiums	

Choose the correct option

4.4   You have been asked to set up a Standing Order authority, using the details set out below. You will not have to sign it or date it. Your business and bank details are already on the form.

> **Hunter Limited: Office Rental Payments**
>
> 12 monthly instalments of £1,500.00 to Ace Properties from 15 January 20XX, under reference EE1934.
>
> Bank details Ventura Bank, Persham, Sort Code 69 98 15, Account 34512358.

STANDING ORDER MANDATE

To ___Mercia_____ Bank

Address _45 Market Street, Persham, PE4 8CV_____

PLEASE PAY TO

Bank _____   Branch _____   Sort code [   ]

Beneficiary _____   Account number [   ]

The sum of £[   ]   Amount in words _____

Date of first payment _____   Frequency of payment _____

Until _____   Reference _____

Account to be debited [Hunter Limited]   Account number [22472434]

SIGNATURE(S)   ....

5 **Chapter activities**
Cash book

5.1   Which one of the following transactions will be recorded on the receipts side of cash book?

	✔
bank charges for £55	
payment of VAT to HM Revenue and Customs for £1,820	
BACS transfer from a customer for £1,950	
drawings made by the owner of the business for £750	

5.2   Which one of the following transactions will be recorded on the payments side of cash book?

	✔
repayment of VAT by HM Revenue and Customs for £255	
BACS transfer from a customer for £690	
debit card payment to a supplier for £940	
increase in owner's capital by bank transfer for £5,000	

5.3 Show whether the following statements are true or false.

Statement		True ✓	False ✓
(a)	Cash and bank control accounts are the general ledger accounts when cash book is used as a book of prime entry only		
(b)	The purchases ledger column total from cash book is credited to purchases ledger control account in general ledger		
(c)	The discount allowed column total from cash book is credited to discount allowed account in general ledger		
(d)	The VAT column total on the payments side of cash book is debited to VAT account in general ledger		

5.4 You are an accounts assistant at Denison Limited. One of your duties is to write-up the cash book.

There are five payments to be entered in Denison Limited's cash book.

Receipts for cash payments

Received cash with thanks for goods bought.
From Denison Ltd, a customer without a credit account.

Net	£40
VAT	£8
Total	£48
Clark & Co	

Received cash with thanks for goods bought.
From Denison Ltd, a customer without a credit account.

Net	£160
VAT	£32
Total	£192
T Kinnear	

Bank payments

Gaskin Ltd
(Purchases ledger account PL110)
£1,690
Note: £15 settlement (cash) discount taken

Bristow Stationery
(No credit account with this supplier)
£144 including VAT

Roussouw & Co
(Purchases ledger account PL280)
£1,140
Note: no settlement (cash) discount taken

(a) Enter the details from the two receipts for cash payments and the three bank payments into the credit side of the cash book shown below and total each column.

Cash book – credit side

Details	Discount	Cash	Bank	VAT	Payables (creditors)	Cash purchases	Stationery expenses
Balance b/f							
Clark & Co							
T Kinnear							
Gaskin Ltd							
Bristow Stationery							
Roussouw & Co							
Totals							

There are two bank receipts from credit customers to be entered in Denison Limited's cash book:

Passmores £455

S McNulty   £833 Note: £15 settlement (cash) discount taken

(b) Enter the above details into the debit side of the cash book and total each column.

Cash book – debit side

Details	Discount	Cash	Bank	Receivables (debtors)
Balance b/f		642	1,022	
Passmores				
S McNulty				
Totals				

(c)   Using your answers to (a) and (b) above, calculate the cash balance.

£

(d)   Using your answers to (a) and (b) above, calculate the bank balance.

£

(e)   Will the bank balance calculated in (d) above be a debit or credit balance?

	✓
Debit	
Credit	

6 **Chapter activities**
Bank reconciliation statements

6.1 Upon receipt of a bank statement, which one of the following must be written into the firm's cash book?

	✔
payment debited in error by the bank	
unpresented cheques	
BACS transfers from customers	
outstanding lodgements	

6.2 A firm's bank statement shows an overdraft of £600. Unpresented cheques total £250; outstanding lodgements total £1,000. What is the balance at bank shown by the cash book?

	✔
£150 debit	
£650 debit	
£250 credit	
£150 credit	

6.3 Show whether the following statements are true or false.

	Statement	True ✓	False ✓
(a)	Some differences between the bank statement and the cash book are described as timing differences – these are not corrected in the cash book		
(b)	A customer's cheque has been dishonoured and returned by the bank – the amount of the returned cheque must be recorded in cash book on the debit side		
(c)	In a bank reconciliation statement which starts with the balance as per bank statement, unpresented cheques are deducted		
(d)	The opening cash book balance at bank will always be the same as the opening bank statement balance		

6.4 On 30 June Martinez & Co received the following bank statement as at 27 June 20-4.

BANK STATEMENT				
Date 20-4	Details	Paid out £	Paid in £	Balance £
01 Jun	Balance brought forward			2,685 C
02 Jun	Cheque 784342	855		1,830 C
07 Jun	BACS credit: P Parker		1,525	3,355 C
08 Jun	Cheque 784344	697		2,658 C
10 Jun	Cheque 784345	1,922		736 C
14 Jun	Paid into bank		2,607	3,343 C
15 Jun	Cheque 784343	412		2,931 C
18 Jun	BACS credit: Watson Ltd		2,109	5,040 C
24 Jun	Direct debit: First Electric	112		4,928 C
24 Jun	Cheque 784347	1,181		3,747 C
25 Jun	Bank charges	45		3,702 C
26 Jun	Cheque 784348	594		3,108 C
D = Debit C = Credit				

The cash book as at 27 June 20-4 is shown below.

CASH BOOK

Date 20-4	Details	Bank £	Date 20-4	Cheque	Details number	Bank £
01 Jun	Balance b/f	1,830	03 Jun	784343	Gladysz & Co	412
05 Jun	P Parker	1,525	03 Jun	784344	Daley Ltd	697
10 Jun	Dunlevy Ltd	2,607	03 Jun	784345	Ward & Lamb	1,922
25 Jun	Corline Traders	1,433	12 Jun	784346	Hendrie Stores	692
26 Jun	Moss & Co	786	12 Jun	784347	McCabes	1,181
			12 Jun	784348	Rehman Ltd	594
			24 Jun		First Electric	112
			25 Jun	784349	Hannaford & Co	764

(a)   Check the items on the bank statement against the items in the cash book.

(b)   Enter any items in the cash book as needed.

(c)   Total the cash book and clearly show the balance carried down at 27 June (closing balance) and brought down at 28 June (opening balance).

Select your entries for the 'Details' column from the following list: Balance b/f, Balance c/d, Bank charges, Closing balance, Corline Traders, Daley Ltd, Dunlevy Ltd, First Electric, Gladysz & Co, Hannaford & Co, Hendrie Stores, McCabes, Moss & Co, Opening balance, P Parker, Rehman Ltd, Ward & Lamb, Watson Ltd.

(d)   Complete the bank reconciliation statement as at 27 June.

Select your entries for the 'Details' column from the following list: Bank charges, Corline Traders, Daley Ltd, Dunlevy Ltd, First Electric, Gladysz & Co, Hannaford & Co, Hendrie Stores, McCabes, Moss & Co, P Parker, Rehman Ltd, Ward & Lamb, Watson Ltd.

Bank reconciliation statement as at 27 June 20-4	
Balance as per bank statement	£
Add	
Name:	£
Name:	£
Total to add	£
Less	
Name:	£
Name:	£
Total to subtract	£
Balance as per cash book	£

Chapter activities
7 Petty cash book

7.1 A firm's petty cash book is operated on the imprest system. The imprest amount is £250. At the end of a particular period, the analysis columns are totalled as follows: VAT £13.42; postage £29.18; travel £45.47; stationery £33.29; cleaning £18.54.

How much cash will be required to restore the imprest amount for the next period?

	✔
£250.00	
£126.48	
£139.90	
£110.10	

7.2 A firm's petty cash book is operated on the imprest system. The imprest amount is £125. At the end of a particular period the petty cash remaining comprised:

2 x £10 notes, 5 x £5 notes, 4 x £1 coins, 3 x 50p coins, 6 x 20p coins, 3 x 10p coins, 3 x 5p coins, 8 x 1p coins.

Provided no errors or discrepancies have occurred, what is the amount of payments that will be recorded in the petty cash book for the period?

	✔
£72.77	
£52.23	
£72.65	
£125.00	

7.3   As petty cashier you are able to authorise payments up to £10.00 each. You are to prepare petty cash vouchers under today's date using the vouchers shown below.

- £4.80, plus VAT, claimed by Melissa Shaw for marker pens bought for use in the office.
- £9.60, including VAT, claimed by Brian Walsh for a taxi fare used on a business visit to a customer, Gowers Limited.

Number the vouchers, beginning with number 459, and date them today.

State the documentation you will require to be attached to each voucher.

petty cash voucher		number	
		date	
description		amount	
		£	p
	VAT at 20%		
signature			
authorised			

Documentation: _____

petty cash voucher		number	
		date	
description		amount	
		£	p
	VAT at 20%		
signature			
authorised			

Documentation: _____

7.4 This is a summary of petty cash payments made by Dalbeith & Co:

Post office paid	£10.70 (no VAT)
City Taxis paid	£14.40 including VAT at 20%
Repair Shop Ltd paid	£18.80 plus VAT at 20%

(a) **Enter the above transactions, in the order in which they are shown, in the petty cash book below.**

(b) **Total the petty cash book and show the balance carried down.**

Select your entries for the 'Details' columns from the following list: Amount, Balance b/f, Balance c/d, City Taxis, Details, Postage, Post office, Repairs, Repair Shop Ltd, Travel, VAT.

Petty cash book

Debit side		Credit side					
Details	Amount £	Details	Amount £	VAT £	Postage £	Travel £	Repairs £
Balance b/f	150.00						

7.5   You are an accounts assistant at Lockton Traders.

Two amounts have been paid from petty cash:

- A4 copier paper for £15.60 plus VAT at 20%
- Taxi fare for £19.20 including VAT at 20%

(a)   **Complete the petty cash vouchers below.**

Petty cash voucher	
Date:	17.04.20-5
Number:	PCV241

A4 copier paper	
Net	£
VAT	£
Gross	£

Petty cash voucher	
Date:	17.04.20-5
Number:	PCV242

Taxi to visit clients	
Net	£
VAT	£
Gross	£

Part way through the month, the petty cash account had a balance of £93.30. The cash in the petty cash box was checked and the following notes and coins were present.

Notes and coins	£
4 x £10 notes	40.00
7 x £5 notes	35.00
9 x £1 coins	9.00
13 x 50p coins	6.50
10 x 10p coins	1.00
17 x 5p coins	0.85

(b)   **Reconcile the cash amount in the petty cash box with the balance on the petty cash account.**

Amount in petty cash box	£
Balance on petty cash account	£
Difference	£

At the end of the month the cash in the petty cash box was £45.65.

(c)   **Complete the petty cash reimbursement below to restore the imprest amount of £175.**

Petty cash reimbursement	
Date: 30.04.20-5	
Amount required to restore the cash in the petty cash box	£

8 Chapter activities
Using control accounts

8.1 You have the following information for the month:

- customer balances at start of month   £25,685
- credit sales   £18,732
- sales returns   £876
- money received from customers   £17,455
- discounts allowed   £227
- bad debt written off   £175

What is the figure for customer balances at the end of the month?

	✔
£23,130	
£25,684	
£25,686	
£26,034	

8.2 You have the following information for the month:

- supplier balances at start of month   £13,278
- credit purchases   £9,584
- purchases returns   £821
- money paid to suppliers   £10,058
- discounts received   £247

What is the figure for supplier balances at the end of the month?

	✔
£12,230	
£13,378	
£11,736	
£14,820	

8.3   You have the following information for the month:

- balance of VAT account at start of month   £2,380   credit
- VAT from sales day book   £1,420
- VAT from purchases day book   £1,065
- VAT from sales returns day book   £223
- VAT from purchases returns day book   £185
- VAT from cash sales   £592

What is the balance of VAT account at the end of the month?

	✔
£1,471 debit	
£1,471 credit	
£3,289 debit	
£3,289 credit	

8.4 You work as an accounts assistant for Tilsley Trading. Today you are working on the purchases ledger control account and purchases ledger.

A summary of transactions with credit suppliers during the month of June is shown below.

(a) **Show whether each entry will be a debit or a credit in the purchases ledger control account in the general ledger.**

Details	Amount	Debit	Credit
	£	✔	✔
Balance of credit suppliers at 1 June	35,106		
Goods bought on credit	20,354		
Payments made to credit suppliers	19,062		
Discounts received	289		
Goods returned to credit suppliers	1,374		

(b) **What will be the balance brought down on 1 July on the above account?**

	✔
Dr £34,735	
Cr £34,735	
Dr £35,477	
Cr £35,477	
Dr £35,313	
Cr £35,313	

The following credit balances were in the purchases ledger on 1 July.

	£
Cockerill Ltd	9,262
Darnbrook & Co	3,495
M Warren	5,724
De Graaf Ltd	6,098
Hannaford Trading	4,477
Quesne plc	5,386

(c) **Reconcile the balances shown above with the purchases ledger control account balance calculated in part (b).**

	£
Balance on purchases ledger control account at 30 June	
Total of the purchases ledger balances at 30 June	
Difference	

(d) **What may have caused the difference you calculated in part (c)?**

	✔
Settlement (cash) discount was entered twice in the purchases ledger control account	
A credit note was not entered in the purchases ledger control account	
A credit note was not entered in the purchases ledger	
Settlement (cash) discount was not entered in the purchases ledger	

(e) **Which one of the following statements is true?**

	✔
Reconciliation of the purchases ledger control account assures managers that the amount showing as outstanding to suppliers is correct.	
Reconciliation of the purchases ledger control account assures managers that the amount showing as outstanding from customers is correct.	
Reconciliation of the purchases ledger control account will show if a sales invoice has been omitted from the purchases ledger.	
Reconciliation of the purchases ledger control account will show if a sales invoice has been omitted from the sales ledger.	

8.5 You work as an accounts assistant for Craven Cottages Ltd. Today you are working on the VAT control account.

The following figures have been taken from Craven Cottages' books of prime entry:

Totals for quarter

Sales day book	
Net	£68,800
VAT	£13,760
Gross	£82,560

Purchases day book	
Net	£35,600
VAT	£7,120
Gross	£42,720

Sales returns day book	
Net	£2,240
VAT	£448
Gross	£2,688

Purchases returns day book	
Net	£1,640
VAT	£328
Gross	£1,968

Cash book: cash sales	
Net	£2,840
VAT	£568
Gross	£3,408

(a) **What will be the entries in the VAT control account to record the VAT transactions in the quarter?**

Select your entries for the 'Details' columns from the following list: Cash sales, Purchases, Purchases day book, Purchases returns, Purchases returns day book, Sales, Sales day book, Sales returns, Sales returns day book, Value Added Tax.

VAT control

Details	Amount £	Details	Amount £

(b) **The VAT return has been completed and shows an amount owing to HM Revenue and Customs of £6,432.**

Is the VAT return correct?

	✓
Yes	
No	

9 Chapter activities
The journal

9.1 Which one of the following transactions will be recorded in the journal?

	✔
purchase of goods on credit	
payroll transactions	
goods returned by a credit customer	
sale of goods for cash	

9.2 Mohammed Pazir started in business on 1 February 20-4 with the following assets and liabilities:

	£
Vehicle	6,500
Fixtures and fittings	2,800
Inventory (stock)	4,100
Cash	150
Bank	1,250
Loan from uncle	5,000

Use the form below to prepare Mohammed's opening journal entry, showing clearly his capital at 1 February 20-4.

Date	Details	Reference	Dr £	Cr £
20-4				

9.3 You are employed by Sachdev Supplies as an accounts assistant. Today the accounts supervisor tells you that a credit customer, Lefroy Limited, has ceased trading, owing Sachdev Supplies £560 plus VAT at 20%.

(a) **Record the journal entries needed in the general ledger to write off the net amount and the VAT.**

Select your account name from the following list: Bad debts, Lefroy Limited, Purchases, Purchases ledger control, Sachdev Supplies, Sales, Sales ledger control, Value Added Tax.

Account name	Amount £	Debit ✓	Credit ✓

(b) **Sachdev Supplies has started a new business, Sachdev Developments, and a new set of accounts is to be opened. A partially completed journal to record the opening entries is shown below.**

Record the journal entries needed in the accounts in the general ledger of Sachdev Developments to deal with the opening entries.

Account name	Amount £	Debit ✔	Credit ✔
Sales ledger control	14,275		
Purchases ledger control	7,392		
Inventory (stock)	4,107		
Office equipment	10,400		
Cash at bank	2,822		
Rent and rates	4,086		
Miscellaneous expenses	794		
Wages	2,397		
Loan from bank	6,250		
Capital	25,239		
Journal to record the opening entries of the new business			

9.4   You are employed by Mullen Limited as an accounts assistant.

Mullen Limited pays its employees through the bank every month and maintains a wages control account. A summary of last month's payroll transactions is shown below.

Item	£
Gross wages	22,352
Income tax	2,510
Employer's National Insurance contributions	1,105
Employees' National Insurance contributions	965
Employer's pension contributions	1,032
Employees' pension contributions	1,032

Record the journal entries needed in the general ledger to:

(a)   **Record the wages expense.**

(b)   **Record HM Revenue and Customs liability.**

(c)   **Record the net wages paid to the employees.**

(d)   **Record the pension fund liability.**

Select your account name from the following list: Bank, Employees' National Insurance, Employer's National Insurance, HM Revenue and Customs, Income tax, Net wages, Pension fund, Wages control, Wages expense.

(a)

Account name	Amount £	Debit ✓	Credit ✓

(b)

Account name	Amount £	Debit ✓	Credit ✓

(c)

Account name	Amount £	Debit ✓	Credit ✓

(d)

Account name	Amount £	Debit ✓	Credit ✓

10   Chapter activities
The trial balance and correction of errors

10.1   Fill in the missing words from the following sentences, choosing from:

omission   commission   principle   original entry   reversal of entries   compensating

(a)   "You made an error of .... when you debited the cost of diesel fuel for the van to Vans Account."

(b)   "I've had an email from the accounts supervisor at Jones Limited concerning the statements of account that we sent out the other day. She says that there is a sales invoice charged that she knows nothing about. I wonder if it should be for T Jones' account and we have made an error of ....?"

(c)   "There is a 'bad figure' on a purchases invoice – we have read it as £35 when it should be £55. It has gone through our accounts wrongly so we have an error of .... to put right."

(d)   "Although the trial balance balanced last week, I've since found an error of £100 in the calculation of the balance of sales account. We will need to check the other balances as I think we may have a .... error."

(e)   "Who was in charge of that trainee last week? He has entered the payment for the electricity bill on the debit side of the bank and on the credit side of electricity – a ...."

(f)   "I found this purchase invoice from last week in amongst the copy statements. As we haven't put it through the accounts we have an error of ...."

10.2 Telephone expenses of £250 paid from the bank have been debited to the bank columns of the cash book and credited to the telephone expenses account. Which one of the following entries will correct the error?

Debit		Credit		✔
Bank	£250	Telephone expenses	£250	
Telephone expenses	£250	Bank	£250	
Bank	£250	Telephone expenses	£250	
Bank	£250	Telephone expenses	£250	
Telephone expenses	£250	Bank	£250	
Telephone expenses	£250	Bank	£250	

10.3   The trial balance of Tairo Traders does not balance. The debit column totals £220,472 and the credit column totals £217,647.

(a)   **What entry will be made in the suspense account to balance the trial balance?**

Account name	Amount £	Debit ✓	Credit ✓
Suspense			

It is important to understand the type of errors that are disclosed by a trial balance and those that are not.

(b)   **Show which of the errors below are, or are not, disclosed by the trial balance.**

Error in the general ledger	Error disclosed by the trial balance ✓	Error NOT disclosed by the trial balance ✓
The cost of diesel fuel, £50, has been debited in the cash book and credited to vehicles account		
A credit sale of £225 has not been entered in the accounts		
The balance of wages account has been calculated incorrectly		
A cash purchase of £85 has been recorded in the cash book only		
The cost of stationery, £54, has been recorded as £45 in the cash book and stationery account		
Rent paid of £450 has been debited to rent paid account and debited in the cash book		

10.4 The initial trial balance of Merrett Marketing at 30 June 20-3 did not balance. The difference of £424 was placed into a suspense account.

The error has been traced to the purchases day book as shown below.

Purchases day book

Date 20-3	Details	Invoice number	Total £	VAT £	Net £
30 Jun	Downing Traders	2798	720	120	600
30 Jun	Morwenna and Co	M/2348	576	96	480
30 Jun	Oades plc	4592	1,248	208	1,040
	Totals		2,120	424	2,120

(a) **Identify the error and record the journal entries needed in the general ledger to:**

(i) **Remove the incorrect entry.**

(ii) **Record the correct entry.**

(iii) **Remove the suspense account balance.**

Select your account name from the following list: Downing Traders, Morwenna and Co, Oades plc, Purchases, Purchases day book, Purchases ledger control, Purchases returns, Purchases returns day book, Sales, Sales day book, Sales ledger control, Sales returns, Sales returns day book, Suspense, Value Added Tax.

(i)

Account name	Amount £	Debit ✔	Credit ✔

(ii)

Account name	Amount £	Debit ✔	Credit ✔

(iii)

Account name	Amount £	Debit ✔	Credit ✔

An entry to record a bank payment of £525 for rent paid has been reversed.

(b) **Record the journal entries needed in the general ledger to:**

(i) **Remove the incorrect entry.**

(ii) **Record the correct entry.**

Select your account name from the following list: Bank, Cash, Purchases, Purchases ledger control, Rent, Sales, Sales ledger control, Suspense, Value Added Tax.

(i)

Account name	Amount £	Debit ✔	Credit ✔

(ii)

Account name	Amount £	Debit ✔	Credit ✔

10.5 The trial balance of Fayer and Co included a suspense account. All the book-keeping errors have now been traced and the journal entries shown below have been recorded.

Journal entries

Account name	Debit £	Credit £
Office expenses	180	
Office equipment		180
Sales returns	295	
Suspense		295
Vehicle expenses	350	
Suspense		350

As the accounts assistant at Fayer and Co, you are to post the journal entries to the general ledger accounts. Dates are not required.

Select your entries for the 'Details' column from the following list: Balance b/f, Office equipment, Office expenses, Sales returns, Suspense, Vehicle expenses.

Office expenses

Details	Amount £	Details	Amount £

Office equipment

Details	Amount £	Details	Amount £

Sales returns

Details	Amount £	Details	Amount £

Suspense

Details	Amount £	Details	Amount £
Balance b/f	645		

Vehicle expenses

Details	Amount £	Details	Amount £

10.6 On 30 June 20-9 Khela Krafts extracted an initial trial balance which did not balance, and a suspense account was opened. On 1 July journal entries were prepared to correct the errors that had been found, and to clear the suspense account. The list of balances in the initial trial balance, and the journal entries to correct the errors, are shown below and on the next page.

As the accounts assistant at Khela Krafts, you are to redraft the trial balance by placing the figures in the debit or credit column. You should take into account the journal entries (on the next page) which will clear the suspense account.

Account name	Balances extracted on 30 June 20-9	Balances at 1 July 20-9	
	£	Debit £	Credit £
Inventory (stock)	8,692		
Sales ledger control	12,347		
Petty cash control	84		
Capital	15,287		
Loan from bank	8,625		
VAT owing to HM Revenue and Customs	2,733		
Purchases ledger control	8,421		
Cash at bank	1,596		
Sales	77,364		
Sales returns	2,913		
Purchases	40,467		
Purchases returns	872		
Wages	20,644		
Advertising	2,397		
Insurance	1,849		
Heating and lighting	1,066		
Rent and rates	3,862		
Vehicle expenses	2,035		
Vehicles	15,400		
Suspense account (credit balance)	50		
Totals			

Journal entries

Account name	Debit £	Credit £
Suspense	490	
Purchases returns		490

Account name	Debit £	Credit £
Suspense	320	
Vehicle expenses		320
Vehicle expenses	230	
Suspense		230

Account name	Debit £	Credit £
Advertising	530	
Suspense		530

Answers to chapter activities

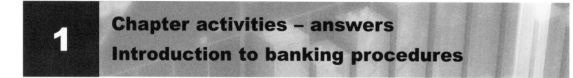

Chapter activities – answers
Introduction to banking procedures

1.1 Banks and building societies offer many similar services.

From the list below tick the services that are offered by banks and/or building societies.

Service	Offered by banks	Offered by building societies
Debit card	✔	✔
Business current account	✔	
Personal current account	✔	✔
House mortgage	✔	✔
Safe custody	✔	
Savings accounts	✔	✔
Investments	✔	✔
Insurance	✔	✔
Personal loan	✔	✔

1.2 6 working days

1.3 six years

1.4 a cheque that a customer has issued but the bank refuses to pay

1.5 a card which can be purchased by a customer and has an amount programmed in which the customer can use up by making purchases

2 Chapter activities – answers
Receiving and recording payments

2.1 **(a)** £351.90

(b) £626.90

(c) £246.00

2.2 **(a)** the cheque is out of date

(b) the amount in words and figures is different

2.3 'Chargeback' in relation to a card payment means that the purchaser who receives faulty or incorrect goods bought using a debit or credit card can claim back the amount paid.

2.4 Card number, expiry date, security code

2.5 **(a)** £980.35

(b) cheque by post, BACS direct bank transfer

(c) cheque - there are no bank details for the money transfer

3 Chapter activities – answers
Paying into the bank

3.1 **(a)** The cheque will need to be returned to the issuer, Capello Designs, and the incorrect amount altered and initialled or signed by the issuer.

(b) The date can be completed by the business paying in the cheque.

3.2 Total of cash £135.46

Total of cheques £249.55

Total of credit £385.01

3.3 **(a)** This payment for £3,430 is a BACS direct credit received from D Guest. It is paid direct to the bank account by computer transfer.

(b) This payment for £2,960 is likely to be receipts from sales on Butterworth Ltd's online shop, paid direct to the bank account.

(c) £3,209.85 CR

4 Chapter activities – answers
Making payments

4.1

Check or procedure	Yes	No
Documents (eg purchase order, delivery note, invoice) checked against each other to make sure they tie up	✔	
Any credit due has been acknowledged in the form of a credit note	✔	
Any remittance advice due has been received		✔
Any discounts due have been allowed by the supplier	✔	
All invoices have been given at least 30 days credit		✔
Payment authorisation has been given	✔	

4.2   make payment of a bill direct to a bank account

4.3   make payments to suppliers

4.4

STANDING ORDER MANDATE

To   Mercia   Bank

Address   45 Market Street, Persham, PE4 8CV

PLEASE PAY TO

Bank Ventura   Branch Persham   Sort code   69 98 15

Beneficiary Ace Properties   Account number   34512358

The sum of   £ 1,500.00   Amount in words   one thousand five hundred pounds only

Date of first payment   15 January 20XX   Frequency of payment   15th Monthly

Until   15 December 20XX   Reference   EE1934

Account to be debited   Hunter Limited   Account number   22472434

SIGNATURE(S)   ....

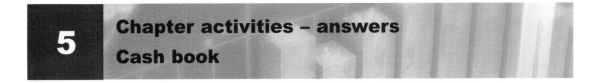

Chapter activities – answers
Cash book

5

5.1 BACS transfer from a customer for £1,950

5.2 debit card payment to a supplier for £940

5.3

Statement		True ✓	False ✓
(a)	Cash and bank control accounts are the general ledger accounts when cash book is used as a book of prime entry only	✓	
(b)	The purchases ledger column total from cash book is credited to purchases ledger control account in general ledger		✓
(c)	The discount allowed column total from cash book is credited to discount allowed account in general ledger		✓
(d)	The VAT column total on the payments side of cash book is debited to VAT account in general ledger	✓	

5.4 **(a)** **Cash book – credit side**

Details	Discount	Cash	Bank	VAT	Payables (creditors)	Cash purchases	Stationery expenses
Balance b/f							
Clark & Co		48		8		40	
T Kinnear		192		32		160	
Gaskin Ltd	15		1,690		1,690		
Bristow Stationery			144	24			120
Roussouw & Co			1,140		1,140		
Totals	15	240	2,974	64	2,830	200	120

(b) **Cash book – debit side**

Details	Discount	Cash	Bank	Receivables (debtors)
Balance b/f		642	1,022	
Passmores			455	455
S McNulty	15		833	833
Totals	15	642	2,310	1,288

(c) £402

(d) £664

(e)

Debit	
Credit	✓

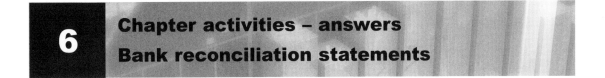

6
Chapter activities – answers
Bank reconciliation statements

6.1 BACS transfers from customers

6.2 £150 debit

6.3

Statement		True ✓	False ✓
(a)	Some differences between the bank statement and the cash book are described as timing differences – these are not corrected in the cash book	✓	
(b)	A customer's cheque has been dishonoured and returned by the bank – the amount of the returned cheque must be recorded in cash book on the debit side		✓
(c)	In a bank reconciliation statement which starts with the balance as per bank statement, unpresented cheques are deducted	✓	
(d)	The opening cash book balance at bank will always be the same as the opening bank statement balance		✓

6.4   (a) – (c)

CASH BOOK

Date 20-4	Details	Bank £	Date 20-4	Cheque	Details number	Bank £
01 Jun	Balance b/f	1,830	03 Jun	784343	Gladysz & Co	412
05 Jun	P Parker	1,525	03 Jun	784344	Daley Ltd	697
10 Jun	Dunlevy Ltd	2,607	03 Jun	784345	Ward & Lamb	1,922
25 Jun	Corline Traders	1,433	12 Jun	784346	Hendrie Stores	692
26 Jun	Moss & Co	786	12 Jun	784347	McCabes	1,181
18 Jun	Watson Ltd	2,109	12 Jun	784348	Rehman Ltd	594
			24 Jun		First Electric	112
			25 Jun	784349	Hannaford & Co	764
			25 Jun		Bank charges	45
			27 Jun		Balance c/d	3,871
		10,290				10,290
28 Jun	Balance b/d	3,871				

(d)

Bank reconciliation statement as at 27 June 20-4	
Balance as per bank statement	£3,108
Add	
Name: Corline Traders	£1,433
Name: Moss & Co	£786
Total to add	£2,219
Less	
Name: Hendrie Stores	£692
Name: Hannaford & Co	£764
Total to subtract	£1,456
Balance as per cash book	£3,871

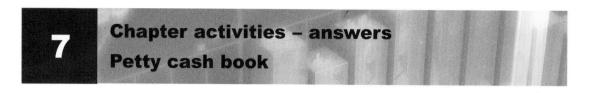

7 Chapter activities – answers
Petty cash book

7.1 £139.90

7.2 £72.77

7.3

petty cash voucher		number **459**		
		date *today*		
description		amount		
			£	p
Marker pens			4	80
			4	80
		VAT at 20%	0	96
			5	76
signature	*Melissa Shaw*			
authorised	*A Student*			

Documentation will be a till receipt from the stationery shop for £5.76, showing the VAT registration number of the stationery shop.

petty cash voucher		number **460**		
		date *today*		
description		amount		
			£	p
Taxi fare re visit to Gowers Ltd			8	00
			8	00
		VAT at 20%	1	60
			9	60
signature	*Brian Walsh*			
authorised	*A Student*			

Documentation will be a receipt from the taxi company for £9.60, showing the VAT registration number of the taxi company.

7.4

Petty cash book

Debit side		Credit side					
Details	**Amount** **£**	**Details**	**Amount** **£**	**VAT** **£**	**Postage** **£**	**Travel** **£**	**Repairs** **£**
Balance b/f	150.00	Post office	10.70		10.70		
		City Taxis	14.40	2.40		12.00	
		Repair Shop Ltd	22.56	3.76			18.80
		Balance c/d	102.34				
	150.00		150.00	6.16	10.70	12.00	18.80

7.5 **(a)**

Petty cash voucher	
Date:	17.04.20-5
Number:	PCV241
A4 copier paper	
Net	£15.60
VAT	£ 3.12
Gross	£18.72

Petty cash voucher	
Date:	17.04.20-5
Number:	PCV242
Taxi to visit clients	
Net	£16.00
VAT	£ 3.20
Gross	£19.20

(b)

Amount in petty cash box	£92.35
Balance on petty cash account	£93.30
Difference	£ 0.95

(c)

Petty cash reimbursement	
Date: 30.04.20-5	
Amount required to restore the cash in the petty cash box	£129.35

8 Chapter activities – answers
Using control accounts

8.1 £25,684

8.2 £11,736

8.3 £3,289 credit

8.4

(a)

Details	Amount £	Debit ✔	Credit ✔
Balance of credit suppliers at 1 June	35,106		✔
Goods bought on credit	20,354		✔
Payments made to credit suppliers	19,062	✔	
Discounts received	289	✔	
Goods returned to credit suppliers	1,374	✔	

(b)

Cr £34,735	✔

(c)

	£
Balance on purchases ledger control account at 30 June	34,735
Total of the purchases ledger balances at 30 June	34,442
Difference	293

(d)

A credit note was not entered in the purchases ledger control account	✔

(e)

Reconciliation of the purchases ledger control account assures managers that the amount showing as outstanding to suppliers is correct.	✔

8.5   (a)

VAT control

Details	Amount £	Details	Amount £
Purchases	7,120	Sales	13,760
Sales returns	448	Purchases returns	328
		Cash sales	568

(b)

Yes	
No	✔

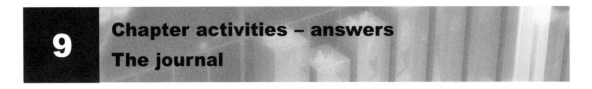

9 **Chapter activities – answers**

The journal

9.1 payroll transactions

9.2

Date	Details	Reference	Dr	Cr
20-4			£	£
1 Feb	Vehicle	GL	6,500	
	Fixtures and fittings	GL	2,800	
	Inventory (stock)	GL	4,100	
	Cash	CB	150	
	Bank	CB	1,250	
	Loan from uncle	GL		5,000
	Capital	GL		9,800
			14,800	14,800
	Assets and liabilities at the start of business			

9.3 **(a)**

Account name	Amount £	Debit ✓	Credit ✓
Bad debts	560	✓	
Value Added Tax	112	✓	
Sales ledger control	672		✓

(b)

Account name	Amount £	Debit ✓	Credit ✓
Sales ledger control	14,275	✓	
Purchases ledger control	7,392		✓
Inventory (stock)	4,107	✓	
Office equipment	10,400	✓	
Cash at bank	2,822	✓	
Rent and rates	4,086	✓	
Miscellaneous expenses	794	✓	
Wages	2,397	✓	
Loan from bank	6,250		✓
Capital	25,239		✓
Journal to record the opening entries of the new business			

9.4

(a)

Account name	Amount £	Debit ✓	Credit ✓
Wages expense	24,489	✓	
Wages control	24,489		✓

(b)

Account name	Amount £	Debit ✓	Credit ✓
Wages control	4,580	✓	
HM Revenue and Customs	4,580		✓

(c)

Account name	Amount £	Debit ✓	Credit ✓
Wages control	17,845	✓	
Bank	17,845		✓

(d)

Account name	Amount £	Debit ✓	Credit ✓
Wages control	2,064	✓	
Pension fund	2,064		✓

10   Chapter activities – answers
The trial balance and correction of errors

10.1   (a)   principle

(b)   commission

(c)   original entry

(d)   compensating

(e)   reversal of entries

(f)   omission

10.2

Debit		*Credit*	
Telephone expenses	£250	Bank	£250
Telephone expenses	£250	Bank	£250

10.3

(a)

Account name	Amount £	Debit ✓	Credit ✓
Suspense	2,825		✓

(b)

Error in the general ledger	Error disclosed by the trial balance ✓	Error NOT disclosed by the trial balance ✓
The cost of diesel fuel, £50, has been debited in the cash book and credited to vehicles account		✓
A credit sale of £225 has not been entered in the accounts		✓
The balance of wages account has been calculated incorrectly	✓	
A cash purchase of £85 has been recorded in the cash book only	✓	
The cost of stationery, £54, has been recorded as £45 in the cash book and stationery account		✓
Rent paid of £450 has been debited to rent paid account and debited in the cash book	✓	

10.4

(a)   (i)

Account name	Amount £	Debit ✔	Credit ✔
Purchases ledger control	2,120	✔	

(ii)

Account name	Amount £	Debit ✔	Credit ✔
Purchases ledger control	2,544		✔

(iii)

Account name	Amount £	Debit ✔	Credit ✔
Suspense	424	✔	

(b)   (i)

Account name	Amount £	Debit ✔	Credit ✔
Rent	525	✔	
Bank	525		✔

(ii)

Account name	Amount £	Debit ✔	Credit ✔
Rent	525	✔	
Bank	525		✔

10.5

Office expenses

Details	Amount £	Details	Amount £
Office equipment	180		

Office equipment

Details	Amount £	Details	Amount £
		Office expenses	180

Sales returns

Details	Amount £	Details	Amount £
Suspense	295		

Suspense

Details	Amount £	Details	Amount £
Balance b/f	645	Sales returns	295
		Vehicle expenses	350

Vehicle expenses

Details	Amount £	Details	Amount £
Suspense	350		

10.6

Account name	Balances extracted on 30 June 20-9	Balances at 1 July 20-9	
	£	Debit £	Credit £
Inventory (stock)	8,692	8,692	
Sales ledger control	12,347	12,347	
Petty cash control	84	84	
Capital	15,287		15,287
Loan from bank	8,625		8,625
VAT owing to HM Revenue and Customs	2,733		2,733
Purchases ledger control	8,421		8,421
Cash at bank	1,596	1,596	
Sales	77,364		77,364
Sales returns	2,913	2,913	
Purchases	40,467	40,467	
Purchases returns	872		1,362
Wages	20,644	20,644	
Advertising	2,397	2,927	
Insurance	1,849	1,849	
Heating and lighting	1,066	1,066	
Rent and rates	3,862	3,862	
Vehicle expenses	2,035	1,945	
Vehicles	15,400	15,400	
Suspense account (credit balance)	50	–	–
Totals		113,792	113,792

Basic accounting 2

Practice assessment 1

Time allowance: 2 hours

- This Assessment relates to the accounting system of Active Toys, a manufacturer of children's swings, slides and climbing frames.
- Each task of the Assessment is to be answered separately.
- The rate of Value Added Tax used is 20%.

Section 1

Task 1.1

Active Toys' trial balance does not balance. The debit column totals £350,295 and the credit column totals £362,841.

(a) **What entry will be made in the suspense account to balance the trial balance?**

Account name	Amount £	Debit ✓	Credit ✓
Suspense			

It is important to understand the type of errors that are disclosed by a trial balance and those that are not.

(b) **Show which of the errors below are, or are not, disclosed by the trial balance.**

Error in the general ledger	Error disclosed by the trial balance ✓	Error NOT disclosed by the trial balance ✓
Discount received of £72 has been recorded in the discount received account as £27		
A bank payment to a credit supplier has been omitted from cash book and purchases ledger control account		
Commission received of £150 has been credited to rent received account		
Sales returns of £225 have been credited to sales account		
A bank payment for vehicle repairs has been recorded in the cash book only		
The balance of sales account has been calculated incorrectly		

Task 1.2

A credit customer, Froggatt Limited, has ceased trading, owing Active Toys £920 plus VAT at 20%.

(a) **Record the journal entries needed in the general ledger to write off the net amount and the VAT.**

Select your account name from the following list: Active Toys, Bad debts, Froggatt Limited, Purchases, Purchases ledger control, Sales, Sales ledger control, Value Added Tax.

Account name	Amount £	Debit ✓	Credit ✓

(b) **Active Toys has started a new business, Active Supplies, and a new set of accounts is to be opened. A partially completed journal to record the opening entries is shown below.**

Record the journal entries needed in the accounts in the general ledger of Active Supplies to deal with the opening entries.

Account name	Amount £	Debit ✔	Credit ✔
Cash	250		
Bank overdraft	2,359		
Vehicles	12,500		
Machinery	8,400		
Capital	25,410		
Inventory (stock)	3,987		
Sales ledger control	4,381		
Purchases ledger control	3,326		
Rent and rates	1,085		
Miscellaneous expenses	492		
Journal to record the opening entries of the new business			

Task 1.3

Active Toys pays its employees through the bank every month and maintains a wages control account. A summary of last month's payroll transactions is shown below.

Item	£
Gross wages	35,247
Income tax	4,780
Employer's National Insurance contributions	3,840
Employees' National Insurance contributions	2,860
Employer's pension contributions	1,740
Employees' pension contributions	1,740

Record the journal entries needed in the general ledger to:

(a)   **Record the wages expense.**

(b)   **Record HM Revenue and Customs liability.**

(c)   **Record the net wages paid to the employees.**

(d)   **Record the pension fund liability.**

Select your account name from the following list: Bank, Employees' National Insurance, Employer's National Insurance, HM Revenue and Customs, Income tax, Net wages, Pension fund, Wages control, Wages expense.

(a)

Account name	Amount £	Debit ✓	Credit ✓

(b)

Account name	Amount £	Debit ✓	Credit ✓

(c)

Account name	Amount £	Debit ✓	Credit ✓

(d)

Account name	Amount £	Debit ✓	Credit ✓

Task 1.4

Active Toys' initial trial balance includes a suspense account with a balance of £1,000.

The error has been traced to the purchases day book as shown below.

Purchases day book

Date 20XX	Details	Invoice number	Total £	VAT £	Net £
30 Jun	Maldanado and Co	5916	3,600	600	3,000
30 Jun	Murray Ltd	M/3421	1,680	280	1,400
30 Jun	Bromfield Supplies	B8624	480	80	400
	Totals		4,760	960	4,800

(a) **Identify the error and record the journal entries needed in the general ledger to:**

(i) **Remove the incorrect entry.**

(ii) **Record the correct entry.**

(iii) **Remove the suspense account balance.**

Select your account name from the following list: Bromfield Supplies, Maldanado and Co, Murray Ltd, Purchases, Purchases day book, Purchases ledger control, Purchases returns, Purchases returns day book, Sales, Sales day book, Sales ledger control, Sales returns, Sales returns day book, Suspense, Value Added Tax.

(i)

Account name	Amount £	Debit ✔	Credit ✔

(ii)

Account name	Amount £	Debit ✔	Credit ✔

(iii)

Account name	Amount £	Debit ✔	Credit ✔

An entry to record a bank receipt of £220 for commission received has been reversed.

(b) **Record the journal entries needed in the general ledger to:**

(i) **Remove the incorrect entry.**

(ii) **Record the correct entry.**

Select your account name from the following list: Bank, Cash, Commission received, Purchases, Purchases ledger control, Sales, Sales ledger control, Suspense, Value Added Tax.

(i)

Account name	Amount £	Debit ✔	Credit ✔

(ii)

Account name	Amount £	Debit ✔	Credit ✔

Task 1.5

Active Toys' trial balance included a suspense account. All the book-keeping errors have now been traced and the journal entries shown below have been recorded.

Journal entries

Account name	Debit £	Credit £
Rent received	450	
Rent paid		450
Purchases	500	
Suspense		500
Office expenses	125	
Suspense		125

Post the journal entries to the general ledger accounts. Dates are not required.

Select your entries for the 'Details' column from the following list: Balance b/f, Office expenses, Purchases, Rent paid, Rent received, Suspense.

Rent received

Details	Amount £	Details	Amount £

Rent paid

Details	Amount £	Details	Amount £

Purchases

Details	Amount £	Details	Amount £

Suspense

Details	Amount £	Details	Amount £
Balance b/f	625		

Office expenses

Details	Amount £	Details	Amount £

Task 1.6

On 30 June Active Toys extracted an initial trial balance which did not balance, and a suspense account was opened. On 1 July journal entries were prepared to correct the errors that had been found, and to clear the suspense account. The list of balances in the initial trial balance, and the journal entries to correct the errors, are shown below.

Redraft the trial balance by placing the figures in the debit or credit column. You should take into account the journal entries (on next page) which will clear the suspense account.

Account name	Balances extracted on 30 June £	Balances at 1 July	
		Debit £	Credit £
Vehicles	17,800		
Inventory (stock)	4,925		
Sales ledger control	6,318		
Petty cash control	49		
Capital	18,835		
Loan from bank	3,841		
VAT owing to HM Revenue and Customs	1,596		
Purchases ledger control	4,389		
Bank overdraft	1,497		
Sales	86,833		
Sales returns	2,076		
Purchases	41,783		
Purchases returns	1,086		
Wages	33,965		
Advertising	3,864		
Insurance	1,597		
Heating and lighting	1,326		
Rent and rates	2,847		
Vehicle expenses	1,727		
Suspense account (credit balance)	200		
Totals			

Journal entries

Account name	Debit £	Credit £
Suspense	280	
Bank		280
Suspense	280	
Bank		280

Account name	Debit £	Credit £
Suspense	1,590	
Sales returns		1,590
Sales returns	1,950	
Suspense		1,950

Section 2

Task 2.1

There are five payments to be entered in Active Toys' cash book.

Receipts for cash payments

<table>
<tr><td>

Received cash with thanks for goods bought.

From Active Toys, a customer without a credit account.

Net	£120
VAT	£24
Total	£144

Gower Ltd

</td><td>

Received cash with thanks for goods bought.

From Active Toys, a customer without a credit account.

Net	£80
VAT	£16
Total	£96

P Billingham

</td></tr>
</table>

Bank payments

<table>
<tr><td>

McIntyres

(Purchases ledger account PL450)

£1,700

Note: £25 settlement (cash) discount taken

</td><td>

Bromfield Stationery

(No credit account with this supplier)

£192 including VAT

</td><td>

Kalsi Ltd

(Purchases ledger account PL335)

£845

Note: no settlement (cash) discount taken

</td></tr>
</table>

(a)   **Enter the details from the two receipts for cash payments and the three bank payments into the credit side of the cash book shown below and total each column.**

Cash book – credit side

Details	Discount	Cash	Bank	VAT	Payables (creditors)	Cash purchases	Stationery expenses
Balance b/f			3,078				
Gower Ltd							
P Billingham							
McIntyres							
Bromfield Stationery							
Kalsi Ltd							
Totals							

There are two bank receipts from credit customers to be entered in Active Toys' cash book:

G Brownlow   £1,286

S Barnett   £565 Note: £20 settlement (cash) discount taken

(b)   **Enter the above details into the debit side of the cash book and total each column.**

Cash book – debit side

Details	Discount	Cash	Bank	Receivables (debtors)
Balance b/f		445		
G Brownlow				
S Barnett				
Totals				

(c)　Using your answers to (a) and (b) above, calculate the cash balance.

£

(d)　Using your answers to (a) and (b) above, calculate the bank balance.

£

(e)　Will the bank balance calculated in (d) above be a debit or credit balance?

	✓
Debit	
Credit	

Task 2.2

On 27 June Active Toys received the following bank statement as at 25 June.

Assume today's date is 30 June, unless told otherwise.

BANK STATEMENT				
Date **20XX**	**Details**	**Paid out** £	**Paid in** £	**Balance** £
01 Jun	Balance brought forward			1,487 C
04 Jun	Cheque 114117	395		1,092 C
05 Jun	Cheque 114118	1,310		218 D
05 Jun	BACS credit: Cottle Ltd		4,806	4,588 C
18 Jun	Cheque 114119	2,218		2,370 C
20 Jun	Direct debit: Wyvern Council	235		2,135 C
21 Jun	BACS credit: Bayer Ltd		1,095	3,230 C
21 Jun	BACS credit: Allen plc		2,786	6,016 C
22 Jun	Direct debit: JA Finance	592		5,424 C
22 Jun	Cheque 114121	1,427		3,997 C
24 Jun	Paid into bank		2,108	6,105 C
24 Jun	Bank charges	45		6,060 C
D = Debit C = Credit				

The cash book as at 25 June is shown below.

CASH BOOK

Date 20XX	Details	Bank £	Date 20XX	Cheque number	Details	Bank £
01 Jun	Balance b/f	1,487	01 Jun	114117	Hendric & Co	395
04 Jun	Cottle Ltd	4,806	01 Jun	114118	Harrup & Noyes	1,310
20 Jun	W Waugh	2,108	10 Jun	114119	Farr Ltd	2,218
24 Jun	Pardo Ltd	1,746	18 Jun	114120	Bradnock Trading	1,036
24 Jun	Torre & Co	542	18 Jun	114121	Paxtons	1,427
			18 Jun	114122	Filiaps Ltd	798
			20 Jun		Wyvern Council	235

(a) **Check the items on the bank statement against the items in the cash book.**

(b) **Enter any items in the cash book as needed.**

(c) **Total the cash book and clearly show the balance carried down at 25 June (closing balance) and brought down at 26 June (opening balance).**

Select your entries for the 'Details' column from the following list: Allen plc, Balance b/d, Balance c/d, Bank charges, Bayer Ltd, Bradnock Trading, Closing balance, Cottle Ltd, Farr Ltd, Filiaps Ltd, Harrup & Noyes, Hendric & Co, JA Finance, Opening balance, Pardo Ltd, Paxtons, Torre & Co, W Waugh, Wyvern Council.

Note: You do not need to adjust the accounts in Section 1.

(d)   **Complete the bank reconciliation statement as at 25 June.**

Select your entry for the 'Name' rows from the following list: Allen plc, Bank charges, Bayer Ltd, Bradnock Trading, Cottle Ltd, Farr Ltd, Filiaps Ltd, Harrup & Noyes, Hendric & Co, JA Finance, Pardo Ltd, Paxtons, Torre & Co, W Waugh, Wyvern Council.

Bank reconciliation statement as at 25 June 20XX	
Balance as per bank statement	£
Add	
Name:	£
Name:	£
Total to add	£
Less	
Name:	£
Name:	£
Total to subtract	£
Balance as per cash book	£

Task 2.3

This is a summary of petty cash payments made by Active Toys.

Western Trains paid	£22.50 (no VAT)
Post office paid	£9.60 (no VAT)
Stationery Supplies Ltd paid	£15.60 plus VAT at 20%

(a) **Enter the above transactions, in the order in which they are shown, in the petty cash book below.**

(b) **Total the petty cash book and show the balance carried down.**

Select your entries for the 'Details' columns from the following list: Amount, Balance b/f, Balance c/d, Details, Postage, Post office, Stationery, Stationery Supplies Ltd, Travel, VAT, Western Trains.

Petty cash book

Debit side		Credit side					
Details	Amount £	Details	Amount £	VAT £	Postage £	Travel £	Stationery £
Balance b/f	200.00						

Task 2.4

Two amounts have been paid from petty cash:

- Taxi fare for £14.40 including VAT at 20%.
- Printer cartridge for £16.40 plus VAT at 20%.

(a)   Complete the petty cash vouchers below.

Petty cash voucher	
Date:	04.07.XX
Number:	PCV145

Taxi fare from station	
Net	£
VAT	£
Gross	£

Petty cash voucher	
Date:	04.07.XX
Number:	PCV146

Printer cartridge for SC printer	
Net	£
VAT	£
Gross	£

Part way through the month, the petty cash account had a balance of £98.20. The cash in the petty cash box was checked and the following notes and coins were present.

Notes and coins	£
6 x £10 notes	60.00
4 x £5 notes	20.00
11 x £1 coins	11.00
11 x 50p coins	5.50
15 x 10p coins	1.50
18 x 5p coins	0.90

(b)   Reconcile the cash amount in the petty cash box with the balance on the petty cash account.

Amount in petty cash box	£
Balance on petty cash account	£
Difference	£

At the end of the month the cash in the petty cash box was £28.70.

(c)   Complete the petty cash reimbursement document below to restore the imprest amount of £150.

Petty cash reimbursement	
Date: 31.07.20XX	
Amount required to restore the cash in the petty cash box	£

Task 2.5

This is a summary of transactions with credit suppliers during the month of June.

(a) **Show whether each entry will be a debit or a credit in the purchases ledger control account in the general ledger.**

Details	Amount	Debit	Credit
	£	✔	✔
Balance of credit suppliers at 1 June	18,392		
Goods bought on credit	6,874		
Payments made to credit suppliers	8,937		
Discounts received	154		
Goods returned to credit suppliers	529		

(b) **What will be the balance brought down on 1 July on the above account?**

	✔
Dr £17,012	
Cr £17,012	
Dr £15,646	
Cr £15,646	
Dr £21,138	
Cr £21,138	

The following credit balances were in the purchases ledger on 1 July.

	£
Hamilton Ltd	3,486
Gusson & Co	1,089
Palgrave Supplies	2,627
Ikpusu & Co	4,321
Lorenz Ltd	747
McDiarmid plc	3,961

(c) **Reconcile the balances shown above with the purchases ledger control account balance calculated in part (b).**

	£
Balance on purchases ledger control account at 30 June	
Total of the purchases ledger balances at 30 June	
Difference	

(d) **What may have caused the difference you calculated in part (c)?**

	✔
An invoice was entered twice in the purchases ledger	
A credit note was entered twice in the purchases ledger	
A credit note was not entered in the purchases ledger control account	
Settlement discount was not entered in the purchases ledger control account	

(e) **Which one of the following statements is true?**

	✔
Reconciliation of the purchases ledger control account assures managers that the amount showing as outstanding to suppliers is correct.	
Reconciliation of the purchases ledger control account assures managers that the amount showing as outstanding from customers is correct.	
Reconciliation of the purchases ledger control account will show if a sales return has been omitted from the purchases ledger.	
Reconciliation of the purchases ledger control account will show if a sales return has been omitted from the sales ledger.	

Task 2.6

The following is an extract from Active Toys' books of prime entry:

Totals for quarter

Sales day book	
Net	£74,000
VAT	£14,800
Gross	£88,800

Purchases day book	
Net	£45,400
VAT	£9,080
Gross	£54,480

Sales returns day book	
Net	£1,840
VAT	£368
Gross	£2,208

Purchases returns day book	
Net	£1,240
VAT	£248
Gross	£1,488

Cash book: cash sales	
Net	£1,880
VAT	£376
Gross	£2,256

(a)   **What will be the entries in the VAT control account to record the VAT transactions in the quarter?**

Select your entries for the 'Details' columns from the following list: Cash sales, Purchases, Purchases day book, Purchases returns, Purchases returns day book, Sales, Sales day book, Sales returns, Sales returns day book, Value Added Tax.

VAT control

Details	Amount £	Details	Amount £

(b)   **The VAT return has been completed and shows an amount owing to HM Revenue and Customs of £5,976.**

Is the VAT return correct?

	✓
Yes	
No	

Task 2.7

Banks and building societies offer many similar services.

(a)   From the list below tick the services that are offered by banks and building societies.

Service	Offered by banks ✔	Offered by building societies ✔
Personal current account		
Business current account		
House mortgage		
Business loan		
Savings account		
Safe custody		

(b)   The 2-4-6 cheque clearance cycle states that after a cheque has been paid in . . .

	True ✔	False ✔
Interest may be paid on the amount of the cheque after two working days.		
The amount of the cheque may only be taken out of the bank after four working days.		
The amount of the cheque may only be taken out of the bank after six working days.		
The amount of the cheque paid in is only guaranteed and safe to be withdrawn out of the account after six working days.		
The amount of the cheque paid in is only guaranteed and safe to be withdrawn out of the account after ten working days.		

(c)   The functions of a debit card normally include all of the following: ✔

payment without having to issue a cheque, cash withdrawals, payment deducted from the bank account 7 working days later	
payment without having to issue a cheque, currency withdrawals overseas, payment deducted from the bank account electronically	
payment without having to issue a cheque, cash withdrawals, payment from the bank account by BACS 3 working days later	

Select the correct option.

Task 2.8

(a) A business can make payment in a variety of ways, depending on the type of payment is involved.

Complete the sentence below using the most appropriate words from the list that follows.

      CHAPS   **standing order**   **BACS**   **direct credit**   **petty cash**

A small value payment for office expenses is often made using ....,

whereas a very large payment, to buy property for example, will be made using the

.... system. Businesses often use the .... system for making

irregular .... payments to a supplier's bank account, or regular payments for rent

by means of a ....

(b) Plastic cards such as debit cards and credit cards offer a flexible way of making payment.

'Chip and PIN' is commonly used in a variety of situations. Indicate below in which situations the 'Chip and PIN' process can and cannot be used.

Situation	*YES* ✔	*NO* ✔
Telephone sales		
Internet sales		
In a restaurant		
At a supermarket		

Basic accounting 2

Practice assessment 2

Time allowance: 2 hours

- This Assessment is based on a sample assessment provided by the AAT and is reproduced here with their kind permission.

- This Assessment relates to the accounting system of Kitchen Kuts.

- Each task of the Assessment is to be answered separately.

- The rate of Value Added Tax used is 20%.

Section 1

Task 1.1

Kitchen Kuts' trial balance was extracted and did not balance. The debit column of the trial balance totalled £400,278 and the credit column totalled £420,125.

(a) What entry would be made in the suspense account to balance the trial balance?

Account name	Amount £	Debit ✔	Credit ✔
Suspense			

It is important to understand the types of errors that are disclosed by the trial balance and those that are not.

(b) Show which of the errors below are, or are not, disclosed by the trial balance.

Error in the general ledger	Error disclosed by the trial balance	Error NOT disclosed by the trial balance
Recording a bank payment for heat and light on the debit side of both the bank and heat and light account.		
Recording a payment for motor repairs in the motor vehicles account.		
Recording a sales credit note on the debit side of the sales ledger control account and the credit side of the sales returns account.		
Incorrectly calculating the balance on the rent account.		
Recording a payment by cheque to a creditor in the bank account and purchases ledger only.		
Recording a bank payment of £470 for motor repairs as £4700 in both accounts.		

Task 1.2

A credit customer, B B Brand Ltd, has ceased trading, owing Kitchen Kuts £1560 plus VAT at 20%.

(a) Record the journal entries needed in the general ledger to write off the net amount and the VAT.

Select your account names from the following list:

Bad debts, B B Brand Ltd, Kitchen Kuts, Purchases, Purchases ledger control, Sales, Sales ledger control, VAT.

Account name	Amount £	Debit ✔	Credit ✔

(b) Kitchen Kuts has started a new business, Kitchen Capers, and a new set of accounts are to be opened. A partially completed journal to record the opening entries is shown below.

Record the journal entries needed in the accounts in the general ledger of Kitchen Capers to deal with the opening entries.

Account name	Amount £	Debit ✔	Credit ✔
Cash	150		
Cash at bank	12,350		
Capital	23,456		
Fixtures and Fittings	2,100		
Insurance	825		
Loan from bank	10,000		
Miscellaneous expenses	218		
Motor vehicle	15,650		
Office expenses	613		
Rent and rates	1,550		
Journal to record the opening entries of new business			

Task 1.3

Kitchen Kuts pays its employees by cheque every month and maintains a wages control account. A summary of last month's payroll transactions is shown below:

Item	£
Gross wages	6,236
Employers' NI	730
Employees' NI	620
Income tax	1,808
Trade Union fees	300

Record the journal entries needed in the general ledger to:

(a) Record the wages expense.

(b) Record the HM Revenue and Customs liability.

(c) Record the net wages paid to the employees.

(d) Record the Trade Union liability.

Select your account names from the following list:

Bank, Employees NI, Employers NI, HM Revenue and Customs, Income tax, Net wages, Trade Union, Wages control, Wages expense.

(a)

Account name	Amount £	Debit ✔	Credit ✔

(b)

Account name	Amount £	Debit ✔	Credit ✔

(c)

Account name	Amount £	Debit ✔	Credit ✔

(d)

Account name	Amount £	Debit ✔	Credit ✔

Task 1.4

Kitchen Kuts' initial trial balance includes a suspense account with a balance of £100.

The error has been traced to the sales returns day-book shown below.

Sales returns day-book

Date 20XX	Details	Credit note number	Total £	VAT £	Net £
30 Jun	Barber Bates Ltd	367	720	120	600
30 Jun	GTK Ltd	368	4,320	720	3,600
30 Jun	Peer Prints	369	960	160	800
Totals			6,000	1,100	5,000

(a) Identify the error and record the journal entries needed in the general ledger to:
- (i) Remove the incorrect entry.
- (ii) Record the correct entry.
- (iii) Remove the suspense account balance.

Select your account names from the following list:

Barber Bates Ltd, GTK Ltd, Peer Prints, Purchases, Purchases day-book, Purchases ledger control, Purchases returns, Purchases returns day-book, Sales, Sales day-book, Sales ledger control, Sales returns, Sales returns day-book, Suspense, VAT.

(i)

Account name	Amount £	Debit ✔	Credit ✔

(ii)

Account name	Amount £	Debit ✔	Credit ✔

(iii)

Account name	Amount £	Debit ✔	Credit ✔

An entry to record a bank payment of £350 for heat and light has been reversed.

(b)   Record the journal entries needed in the general ledger to:

(i)   Remove the incorrect entry.

(ii)   Record the correct entry.

Select your account names from the following list:

Bank, Cash, Heat and light, Purchases, Purchases ledger control, Sales, Sales ledger control, Suspense, VAT.

(i)

Account name	Amount £	Debit ✔	Credit ✔

(ii)

Account name	Amount £	Debit ✔	Credit ✔

Task 1.5

Kitchen Kuts' trial balance included a suspense account. All the bookkeeping errors have now been traced and the journal entries shown below have been recorded.

Journal entries

Account name	Debit £	Credit £
Office stationery	167	
Suspense		167
Suspense	1,800	
Rent and rates		1,800
Bank interest received	98	
Bank interest charged		98

Post the journal entries to the general ledger accounts. Dates are not required.

Select your entries for the 'Details' column from the following list:

Balance b/f, Bank interest charged, Bank interest received, Office stationery, Rent and rates, Suspense.

Office stationery

Details	Amount £	Details	Amount £

Rent and rates

Details	Amount £	Details	Amount £

Suspense

Details	Amount £	Details	Amount £
		Balance b/f	1,633

Bank interest received

Details	Amount £	Details	Amount £

Bank interest charged

Details	Amount £	Details	Amount £

Task 1.6

On 30 June, Kitchen Kuts extracted an initial trial balance which did not balance, and a suspense account was opened. On 1 July journal entries were prepared to correct the errors that had been found, and clear the suspense account. The list of balances in the initial trial balance, and the journal entries to correct the errors, are shown below.

Re-draft the trial balance by placing the figures in the debit or credit column. You should take into account the journal entries which will clear the suspense account.

	Balances extracted on 30 June £	Balances at 1 July Debit £	Credit £
Motor vehicles	34,536		
Fixtures and fittings	17,350		
Stock	7,300		
Bank overdraft	5,521		
Petty cash	100		
Sales ledger control	100,625		
Purchases ledger control	56,119		
VAT owing to HM Revenue and Customs	8,300		
Capital	22,844		
Sales	222,955		
Purchases	112,250		
Purchases returns	6,780		
Wages	25,700		
Motor expenses	1,368		
Office expenses	3,354		
Rent and rates	1,444		
Heat and light	2,155		
Insurance	3,165		
Miscellaneous expenses	2,220		
Suspense account (debit balance)	10,952		
Totals			

Journal entries

Account name	Debit £	Credit £
Bank	5,521	
Suspense		5,521
Bank	5,521	
Suspense		5,521

Account name	Debit £	Credit £
Purchases returns	6,780	
Suspense		6,780
Purchases returns		6,870
Suspense	6,870	

Section 2

Task 2.1

There are five payments to be entered in Kitchen Kuts' cash-book.

Receipts

Received cash with thanks for goods bought. From Kitchen Kuts, a customer without a credit account. Net £200 VAT £40 Total £240 *B. Smithson Ltd*	Received cash with thanks for goods bought. From Kitchen Kuts, a customer without a credit account. Net £160 VAT £32 Total £192 *H Hamnet*

Received cash with thanks for goods bought.

From Kitchen Kuts, a customer without a credit account.

Net   £320

(No VAT)

Renee Reid

Cheque book counterfoils

Tenon Ltd (Purchase ledger account TEN006) £3600 (Note: Have taken £80 settlement discount) 000168	Vernon Motor Repairs (We have no credit account with this supplier) £48 including VAT 000169

(a)   Enter the details from the three receipts and two cheque book stubs into the credit side of the cash-book shown below and total each column.

Cash-book – credit side

Details	Discount	Cash	Bank	VAT	Creditors	Cash purchases	Motor expenses
Balance b/f			16,942				
B. Smithson Ltd							
H Hamnet							
Renee Reid							
Tenon Ltd							
Vernon Motor Repairs							
Total							

There are two cheques from credit customers to be entered in Kitchen Kuts' cash book:

G Brownlow   £749

S Barnett   £300 (this customer has taken a £30 discount)

(b)   Enter the above details into the debit side of the cash-book and total each column.

Cash book – debit side

Details	Discount	Cash	Bank	Debtors
Balance b/f		1,325		
G Brownlow				
S Barnett				
Total				

(c)   Using your answers to (a) and (b) above, calculate the cash balance.

£

(d)   Using your answers to (a) and (b) above, calculate the bank balance.

£

(e)   Will the bank balance calculated in (d) above be a debit or credit balance?

Debit   /   Credit

Task 2.2

On 28 June Kitchen Kuts received the following bank statement as at 23 June.

Assume today's date is 30 June, unless told otherwise.

Midway Bank PLC, 52 The Parade, Darton, DF10 9SW				
To: Kitchen Kuts	Account No 39103988			23 June 20XX
Statement of Account				
Date	Detail	Paid out	Paid in	Balance
2006		£	£	£
04 June	Balance b/f			15,189 C
04 June	Cheque 111042	10,000		5,189 C
04 June	Cheque 111043	1,420		3,769 C
05 June	Cheque 111044	80		3,689 C
06 June	Cheque 111047	2,500		1,189 C
12 June	Bank Giro Credit Cabot and Co		571	1,760 C
13 June	Cheque 111045	795		965 C
13 June	Direct Debit LMBC	150		815 C
20 June	Direct Debit Insurance Direct	850		35 D
23 June	Bank Charges	88		123 D
23 June	Overdraft fee	30		153 D
23 June	Paid in at Midway Bank		175	22 C
D = Debit C = Credit				

Cash book as at 23 June

Date 20XX	Details	Bank £	Date 20XX	Cheque number	Details	Bank £
01 June	Balance b/f	15,189	01 June	111042	Prime kitchens	10,000
16 June	Britten & Bond	175	01 June	111043	Equipdirect	1,420
20 June	Macklin Ltd	950	01 June	111044	Long and Lane	80
21 June	Randle fitments	300	01 June	111045	BLH Ltd	795
			02 June	111046	MVR Ltd	652
			02 June	111047	Fairfield Ltd	2,500
			13 June	111048	Makin and King	450
			13 June		LBMC	150

(a) Check the items on the bank statement against the items in the cash book.

(b) Enter any items in the cash book as needed.

(c) Total the cash book and clearly show the balance carried down at 23 June (closing balance) and brought down at 24 June (opening balance).

Select your entries for the 'Details' column from the following list:

Balance b/d, Balance c/d, Bank charges, BLH Ltd, Britten & Bond, Cabot and Co, Closing balance, Equipdirect, Fairfield Ltd, Insurance Direct, LBMC, Long and Lane, Macklin Ltd, Makin and King, MVR Ltd, Opening balance, Overdraft fees, Prime Kitchens, Randle Fitments

Note:

You do not need to adjust the accounts in Section 1.

(d) Complete the bank reconciliation statement as at 23 June.

Select your entries for the 'Name' rows from the following list:

Bank charges, BLH Ltd, Britten & Bond, Cabot and Co, Equipdirect, Fairfield Ltd, Insurance Direct, LBMC, Long and Lane, Macklin Ltd, Makin and King, MVR Ltd, Overdraft fees, Prime Kitchens, Randle Fitments.

Note: Do not make any entries in the shaded boxes.

Bank reconciliation statement as at 23 June 20XX

	£
Balance per bank statement	£
Add:	
Name:	£
Name:	£
Total to add	£
Less:	
Name:	£
Name:	£
Total to subtract	£
Balance as per cash book	£

Task 2.3

This is a summary of petty cash payments made by Kitchen Kuts.

Tom's Taxi paid	£18.00 (no VAT)
Post Office paid	£30.00 (no VAT)
SMP Stationery paid	£36.00 plus VAT at 20%

(a) Enter the above transactions, in the order in which they are shown, in the petty cash-book below.

(b) Total the petty cash-book and show the balance carried down.

Select your entries for the 'Details' columns from the following list:

Amount, Balance b/d, Balance c/d, Details, Postage, Post Office, Stationery, SMP Stationery, Tom's Taxi, Travel, VAT.

Petty cash-book

Debit side		Credit side					
Details	*Amount* £	*Details*	*Amount* £	*VAT* £	*Postage* £	*Travel* £	*Stationery* £
Balance b/f	150.00						

Task 2.4

Two amounts have been paid from petty cash:

- Envelopes for £16.80 including VAT at 20%.

- Motor fuel for £32.00 plus VAT at 20%.

(a) Complete the petty cash vouchers below.

Petty cash voucher	
Date:	7.07.XX
Number:	PC187
5 packs A4 envelopes	
Net	£
VAT	£
Gross	£

Petty cash voucher	
Date:	7.07.XX
Number:	PC188
Fuel for motor van	
Net	£
VAT	£
Gross	£

Part way through the month, the petty cash account had a balance of £120.00. The cash in the petty cash box was checked and the following notes and coins were present.

Notes and coins	£
3 x £20 notes	60.00
5 x £5 notes	25.00
17 x £1 coins	17.00
23 x 50p coins	11.50
16 x 10p coins	1.60
21 x 5p coins	1.05

(b) Reconcile the cash amount in the petty cash box with the balance on the petty cash account.

Amount in petty cash box	£
Balance on petty cash account	£
Difference	£

At the end of the month the cash in the petty cash box was £3.45.

(c) Complete the petty cash reimbursement document below to restore the imprest amount of £200.

Petty cash reimbursement	
Date: 31.07.20XX	
Amount required to restore the cash in the petty cash box.	£

Task 2.5

This is a summary of transactions with suppliers during the month of June.

(a) Show whether each entry will be a debit or credit in the Purchases ledger control account in the Main ledger.

Details	Amount £	Debit ✔	Credit ✔
Balance of creditors at 1 June	50,530		
Goods bought on credit	17,504		
Payments made to credit suppliers	20,672		
Discount received	392		
Goods returned to credit suppliers	784		

(b) What will be the balance brought down on 1 July on the above account?

	✔
Dr £54,874	
Cr £54,874	
Dr £46,970	
Cr £46,970	
Dr £46,186	
Cr £46,186	

The following credit balances were in the subsidiary (purchases) ledger on 1 July.

	£
MMM Ltd	21,300
Walton Doors Ltd	4,198
Bramble and Barnet	123
Croxford and Company	15,530
Goodman Timber	1,119
Masefield Limited	3,524

(c) Reconcile the balances shown above with the purchases ledger control account balance you have calculated in part (a).

	£
Purchases ledger control account balance as at 30 June	
Total of subsidiary (purchases) ledger accounts as at 30 June	
Difference	

(d)   What may have caused the difference you calculated in part (b)?   ✔

Goods returned may have been omitted from the subsidiary ledger	
Discounts received may have been omitted from the subsidiary ledger	
Goods returned may have been entered in the subsidiary ledger twice	
Discounts received may have been entered in the subsidiary ledger twice	

It is important to reconcile the purchases ledger control account on a regular basis.

(e)   Which of the following statements is true?   ✔

Reconciliation of the purchases ledger control account assures managers that the amount showing as outstanding from customers is correct	
Reconciliation of the purchases ledger control account assures managers that the amount showing as outstanding to suppliers is correct	
Reconciliation of the purchases ledger control account will show if a sales invoice has been omitted from the sales ledger	
Reconciliation of the purchases ledger control account will show if a sales invoice has been omitted from the purchases ledger	

Task 2.6

The following is an extract from Kitchen Kuts' books of prime entry.

Totals for quarter			
Sales day-book		**Purchases day-book**	
Net:	£172,000	Net:	£ 98,000
VAT:	£ 34,400	VAT:	£ 19,600
Gross:	£206,400	Gross:	£ 117,600
Sales returns day-book		**Purchases returns day-book**	
Net:	£ 2,800	Net:	£ 7,600
VAT:	£ 560	VAT:	£ 1,520
Gross:	£ 3,360	Gross:	£ 9,120
Cash book			
Net cash sales:	£320		
VAT:	£ 64		
Gross cash sales:	£384		

(a) What will be the entries in the VAT control account to record the VAT transactions in the quarter?

Select your entries for the 'Details' columns from the following list:

Cash book, Purchases, Purchases day-book, Purchases returns, Purchases returns day-book, Cash sales, Sales day-book, Sales returns, Sales returns day-book, VAT.

VAT control

Details	Amount £	Details	Amount £

The VAT return has been completed and shows an amount owing from HM Revenue and Customs of £15,760.

(b) Is the VAT return correct?   Yes / No

Task 2.7

Banks and building societies offer many similar services.

(a) From the list below select TWO services that are not offered by building societies.

Service	Not offered by building societies ✔
Foreign Currency	
Loan	
Overdraft	
Safe custody	
Savings account	
Telephone banking	

(b) Show whether the following statements are true or false.

	True	False
A bank cheque paid into a building society does not have to pass through the clearing system.		
A building society cheque paid into a bank does not have to pass through the clearing system.		
A bank cheque has to be passed to the bank of the issuer before the money becomes available.		
A building society cheque has to be passed to the bank of the issuer before the money becomes available.		

It is important to understand that banking documents need to be retained by an organisation so that Accountants, HM Revenue and Customs, and other organisations can access them when required.

(c) Which TWO of the documents below are banking documents that must be retained by Kitchen Kuts?

	✔
Aged debtor analysis	
Aged creditor analysis	
Bank statements	
Credit cards	
Debit cards	
Paying in slip stubs	
Remittance advice notes	
Supplier invoices	

Task 2.8

Kitchen Kuts receives payment from customers and makes payments to suppliers in a variety of ways.

(a) Select TWO checks that have to be made on each of the two payment methods shown below when received from customers.

Checks to be made	Cheque	Telephone credit card payment
Check expiry date		
Check issue number		
Check not posted dated		
Check security number		
Check words and figures match		
Check card has not been tampered with		

(b) Show whether each of the statements below is true or false.

	True	False
When Kitchen Kuts makes payments to suppliers by credit card, the amount leaves the bank current account immediately.		
When Kitchen Kuts makes payments to suppliers by debit card, the amount paid does not affect the bank current account.		

Basic accounting 2

Practice assessment 3

Time allowance: 2 hours

- This Assessment relates to the accounting system of Wyvern Trading Limited.
- Each task of the Assessment is to be answered separately.
- The rate of Value Added Tax used is 20%.

Section 1

Task 1.1

Wyvern Trading Ltd's trial balance was extracted and does not balance. The debit column of the trial balance totalled £474,832 and the credit column totalled £473,154.

(a)   What entry would be made in the suspense account to balance the trial balance?

Account name	Amount £	Debit ✓	Credit ✓
Suspense			

It is important to understand the types of errors that can occur within a double-entry system that will not be revealed by the trial balance.

(b)   Match each of the following descriptions with the type of error.

Select from the following types of error: Compensating error, Error of commission, Error of omission, Error of original entry, Error of principle, Reversal of entries.

Description of error	Type of error
Entries have not been made in the general ledger for a transaction.	
An entry has been made in the purchases ledger for the correct amount but it has been recorded in the wrong supplier's account.	
The cost of fuel for vehicles has been recorded correctly in the general ledger, but the vehicles account has been debited.	
Entries in the general ledger have been made in the correct accounts but, instead of £65, the amount has been recorded as £56 in both accounts.	
Entries have been made in the general ledger for a transaction, but on the wrong side of each account.	
The balance of stationery expenses account has been overstated by £100 and the balance of rent received account has been overstated by £100.	

Task 1.2

A credit customer, KJ Francis, has ceased trading, owing Wyvern Trading Ltd £1,872 including VAT.

(a)   **Record the journal entries needed in the general ledger to write off the net amount and the VAT.**

Select your account name from the following list: KJ Francis, Irrecoverable debts, Purchases, Purchases ledger control, Sales, Sales ledger control, Value Added Tax, Wyvern Trading Ltd.

Account name	Amount £	Debit ✓	Credit ✓

Wyvern Trading Ltd has started a new business, Wyvern Supplies Ltd, and a new set of accounts is to be opened. A partially completed journal to record the opening entries is shown below.

(b)   **Complete the journal for each account name by showing whether it will be recorded in the debit or credit column.**

The Journal

Account name	Amount £	Debit ✓	Credit ✓
Bank overdraft	1,524		
Capital	15,500		
Discount allowed	155		
Heat and light	1,084		
Office equipment	5,450		
Purchases	7,894		
Sales	14,466		
Sales ledger control	6,452		
Vehicles	11,500		
VAT owing	1,045		
Journal to record the opening entries of the new business			

Task 1.3

Wyvern Trading Ltd pays its employees by BACS transfer every month and maintains a wages control account. A summary of last month's payroll transactions is shown below.

Item	£
Gross wages	33,471
Income tax	5,196
Employer's NI	2,915
Employees' NI	2,657
Employees' pension contributions	1,200

Record the journal entries needed in the general ledger to:

(a)   Record the wages expense.

(b)   Record the net wages paid to the employees.

(c)   Record the HM Revenue and Customs liability.

(d)   Record the Pension liability.

Select your account name from the following list: Bank, Employees' NI, Employer's NI, HM Revenue and Customs, Income tax, Net wages, Pension, Wages control, Wages expense.

(a)   Record the wages expense

Account name	Amount £	Debit ✓	Credit ✓

(b)   Record the net wages paid to the employees

Account name	Amount £	Debit ✓	Credit ✓

(c)   **Record the HM Revenue and Customs liability**

Account name	Amount £	Debit ✓	Credit ✓

(d)   **Record the Pension liability**

Account name	Amount £	Debit ✓	Credit ✓

Task 1.4

Wyvern Trading Ltd's initial trial balance includes a suspense account.

The error has been traced to the entries made in the cash book and general ledger accounts on 4 June, as shown below.

Cash book – credit side

Date	Details	Discounts	Bank
20XX		£	£
4 June	XJ Ltd (credit supplier)	110	3,415

Purchases ledger control

Date	Details	Amount	Date	Details	Amount
20XX		£	20XX		£
4 June	Bank	3,415			
4 June	Discount	110			

Discounts allowed

Date	Details	Amount	Date	Details	Amount
20XX		£	20XX		£
4 June	Purchases ledger control	110			

(a) Identify the error and record the journal entries needed in the general ledger to:

(i) Remove the incorrect entry.

(ii) Record the correct entry.

(iii) Remove the suspense account balance.

Select your account name from the following list: Bank, Discounts allowed, Discounts received, Purchases, Purchases day book, Purchases ledger control, Purchases returns, Purchases returns day book, Sales, Sales day book, Sales ledger control, Sales returns, Sales returns day book, Suspense, Value Added Tax, XJ Ltd.

(i) Remove the incorrect entry

Account name	Amount £	Debit ✔	Credit ✔

(ii)   Record the correct entry

Account name	Amount £	Debit ✔	Credit ✔

(iii)   Remove the suspense account balance

Account name	Amount £	Debit ✔	Credit ✔

An entry to record a cheque for £450, paid in respect of office expenses, had been reversed.

(b)   Record the journal entries needed in the general ledger to:

(i)   Remove the incorrect entry.

(ii)   Record the correct entry.

Select your account name from the following list: Bank, Cash, Office expenses, Purchases, Purchases ledger control, Sales, Sales ledger control, Suspense, Value Added Tax.

(i)   Remove the incorrect entry

Account name	Amount £	Debit ✔	Credit ✔

(ii)   Record the correct entry

Account name	Amount £	Debit ✔	Credit ✔

Task 1.5

Wyvern Trading Ltd's trial balance included a suspense account. All the bookkeeping errors have now been traced and the journal entries shown below have been recorded.

Journal entries

Account name	Debit £	Credit £
Vehicle expenses	274	
Miscellaneous expenses		274
Office equipment	2,000	
Suspense		2,000
Suspense	1,223	
Wages control		1,223

Post the journal entries to the general ledger accounts.

Select your entries for the 'Details' column from the following list: Miscellaneous expenses, Office equipment, Suspense, Vehicle expenses, Wages control.

Vehicle expenses account

Details	Amount £	Details	Amount £

Miscellaneous expenses account

Details	Amount £	Details	Amount £

Office equipment account

Details	Amount £	Details	Amount £

Suspense account

Details	Amount £	Details	Amount £
Balance b/f	777		

Wages control account

Details	Amount £	Details	Amount £

Task 1.6

On 30 June Wyvern Trading Ltd extracted an initial trial balance which did not balance, and a suspense account was opened with a £507 debit balance. On 1 July, three journal entries were prepared to correct the errors that had been found, and to clear the suspense account. The journal entries to correct the errors and the list of balances in the initial trial balance, are shown below.

Redraft the trial balance by placing the figures in the debit or credit column. You should take into account the journal entries which will clear the suspense account. Do not enter figures with decimal places in this task.

Journal entries

Account name	Debit £	Credit £
Vehicle expenses	314	
Purchases		314

Account name	Debit £	Credit £
Suspense	218	
Commission received		218

Account name	Debit £	Credit £
Office expenses	725	
Suspense		725

Trial balance

Account name	Balances extracted on 30 June £	Debit balances at 1 July £	Credit balances at 1 July £
Bank overdraft	3,525		
Capital	15,000		
Commission received	424		
Discounts received	238		
Heating and lighting	2,475		
Irrecoverable debts written off	419		
Miscellaneous expenses	1,785		
Office expenses	1,616		
Petty cash	250		
Purchases	74,630		
Purchases ledger control	10,721		
Purchases returns	1,047		
Rent paid	3,625		
Sales	117,618		
Sales ledger control	25,032		
Sales returns	3,784		
VAT owing to HM Revenue and Customs	2,419		
Vehicle expenses	5,734		
Wages and salaries	31,135		
Totals			

Section 2

Task 2.1

There are four payments to be entered in Wyvern Trading Ltd's cash book.

Payments to suppliers who do not offer credit accounts:

- cash paid to James Marshall of £252, including VAT, for goods purchased

- a bank payment of £350, no VAT, to Wyvern Council for rates

Payments to credit suppliers:

- BACS payments made as authorised on the two invoices shown below.

<table>
<tr><td>

Blenheim plc
18 Blenheim Road
Linton LT4 6AR
VAT Registration No 315 4692 00

Invoice No. 5742   30 June 20XX

To: Wyvern Trading Ltd
    14 Nelson Street
    Linton, LT2 8TY

                                      £
100 items of XJ @ £5.00 each   500.00
VAT @ 20%   98.00
Total   598.00

Authorised for payment of £588, £10
settlement discount taken: N Rose

Terms: 2% settlement discount for payment in 10 days or 30 days net.

</td><td>

K. Bialas
1 Henry Street
Linton LT3 4YK
VAT Registration No 474 3918 00

Invoice No. I3946   30 June 20XX

To: Wyvern Trading Ltd
    14 Nelson Street
    Linton, LT2 8TY

                                      £
75 items of XL @ £6.00 each   600.00
VAT @ 20%   120.00
Total   720.00

Authorised for payment in full: N Rose

Terms: 30 days net.

</td></tr>
</table>

(a) **Enter the details of the four payments into the credit side of the cash book shown below and total each column.**

Select your entries for the 'Details' column from the following list: AGS Supplies, K. Bialas, Blenheim plc, James Marshall, Tyax plc, Tom Walton, Wyvern Council.

Cash book – credit side

Details	Discount	Cash	Bank	VAT	Trade Payables	Cash purchases	Other expenses
	£	£	£	£	£	£	£
Balance b/f			5,218				
Total							

There are three amounts received to be entered in Wyvern Trading Ltd's cash book.

Cheques received from credit customers:

· AGS Supplies £1,345

· Tyax plc £2,312 (this customer has taken a £40 settlement discount)

Cash received:

· £350 received from Tom Walton for rent of office space (No VAT)

(b) **Enter the above details into the debit side of the cash book and total each column.**

Select your entries for the 'Details' column from the following list: AGS Supplies, K. Bialas, Blenheim plc, James Marshall, Tyax plc, Tom Walton, Wyvern Council.

Cash book – debit side

Details	Discount	Cash	Bank	Trade Receivables	Other income
	£	£	£	£	£
Balance b/f		356			
Total					

(c)   Using your answers to (a) and (b) above, calculate the cash balance. Do not use commas when entering figures in this part of the question.

£

(d)   Using your answers to (a) and (b) above, calculate the bank balance. If your calculations show that the bank account is overdrawn your answer should start with a minus sign, for example -123. Do not use commas when entering figures in this part of the question.

£

(e)   What will be the entry in Blenheim plc's account in the purchases ledger to record the discount received?

Purchases ledger

Account name	Amount £	Debit ✔	Credit ✔
Blenheim plc			

Task 2.2

On 27 July Wyvern Trading Ltd received the following bank statement as at 25 July.

	WESTERN BANK PLC			
	20 High Street, Linton, LT1 4AB			
To: Wyvern Trading Ltd	Account no: 47813292			25 July 20XX
BANK STATEMENT				
Date 20XX	Details	Paid out £	Paid in £	Balance £
01 July	Balance b/f			2,106 D
01 July	BACS transfer: Southern Supplies		1,249	
01 July	Cheque 017629	674		1,531 D
05 July	BACS transfer: Fogg plc		2,314	783 C
18 July	Cheque 017631	483		300 C
20 July	Direct debit: TP Ltd	565		265 D
21 July	BACS transfer: Trader Bills Ltd		854	
21 July	Paid into bank		1,716	2,305 C
22 July	Standing order: Linton insurance	420		
22 July	Cheque 017632	1,126		759 C
24 July	Bank charges	126		
24 July	BACS transfer: C & D plc		2,858	3,491 C
D = Debit C = Credit				

The cash book as at 25 July is shown below.

CASH BOOK

Date 20XX	Details	Bank £	Date 20XX	Cheque number	Details	Bank £
04 Jul	Fogg plc	2,314	01 Jul		Balance b/f	1,531
19 Jul	Trader Bills Ltd	854	02 Jul	017630	Bokova Ltd	652
21 Jul	Winton plc	1,716	05 Jul	017631	Palacions Sisters	483
24 Jul	Jamieson Partners	568	15 Jul	017632	Ikpasa plc	1,126
25 Jul	Coopers	2,382	24 Jul	017633	Patel & Sons	210

(a)   **Check the items on the bank statement against the items in the cash book.**

(b)   **Enter any items in the cash book as needed.**

(c)   **Total the cash book and clearly show the balance carried down at 25 July *and* brought down at 26 July.**

Select your entries for the 'Details' column from the following list:

Balance b/d, Balance c/d, Bank charges, Bokova Ltd, C & D plc, Cheque 017629, Coopers, Fogg plc, Ikpasa plc, Jamieson Partners, Linton Insurance, Palacions Sisters, Patel & Sons, Southern Supplies, TP Ltd, Trader Bills Ltd, Winton plc.

(d) **Complete the bank reconciliation statement as at 25 July.**

Select your entry for the 'Name' rows from the following list:

Bank charges, Bokova Ltd, C & D plc, Cheque 017629, Coopers, Fogg plc, Ikpasa plc, Jamieson Partners, Linton Insurance, Palacions Sisters, Patel & Sons, Southern Supplies, TP Ltd, Trader Bills Ltd, Winton plc.

Bank reconciliation statement as at 25 July 20XX	
Balance as per bank statement	£
Add	
Name:	£
Name:	£
Total to add	£
Less	
Name:	£
Name:	£
Total to subtract	£
Balance as per cash book	£

Task 2.3

This is a summary of petty cash payments made by Wyvern Trading Ltd during one week.

Taxi fare paid	£18.60 including VAT
Postage paid	£10.40 (no VAT)
Envelopes purchased	£13.40 plus VAT

(a) **Enter the above transactions in the petty cash book below.**

(b) **Total the petty cash book and show the balance carried down.**

Select your entries for the 'Money' columns from the following list:

(note that each item can be used more than once; you may not need to use all of the items): £150.00, £110.70, £104.92, £45.08, £39.30, £18.60, £16.08, £15.50, £13.40, £10.40, £5.78, £3.10, £2.68, £2.08.

Petty cash book

Debit side		Credit side					
Details	Amount £	Details	Amount £	VAT £	Postage £	Travel £	Stationery £
Balance b/f	150.00	Taxi fare					
		Post office					
		Envelopes					
		Balance c/d					

Task 2.4

Wyvern Trading Ltd operates a petty cash system with an imprest amount of £250.

On 1 July, the cash in the petty cash box was £90.58

(a) **Complete the petty cash reimbursement document below to restore the imprest amount.**

Petty cash reimbursement	
Date: 01.07.20XX	
Amount required to restore the cash in the petty cash box	£

On 3 July the following receipt was presented for payment from petty cash.

Linton Office Supplies Cash receipt 157
Date: 04.07.20XX
Cash received for the purchase of stationery, £24.30, including VAT.
Henry Winter Cashier

(b) **Complete the petty cash voucher below.**

Petty cash voucher
Date: 03.07.20XX Number: PC642
Stationery Net   £ VAT   £ Gross   £

By 31 July further amounts totalling £164.27 have been paid from petty cash.

(c) **What is the balance on the petty cash account on 31 July?**

£

The cash in the petty cash box on 31 July was checked and the following notes and coins were there.

(d) **Insert the missing figures to complete the table and show the total amount in the petty cash box.**

Notes and coins	£
1 x £10 notes	10.00
5 x £5 notes	25.00
5 x £2 coins	10.00
9 x £1 coins	9.00
4 x 50p coins	2.00
17 x 20p coins	
12 x 5p coins	
17 x 2p coins	
TOTAL	

(e) **What is the difference between the balance on the petty cash account and the total amount of cash in the petty cash box on 31 July?**

£

Task 2.5

At the end of June, the sales ledger control account had debit entries amounting to £84,347 and credit entries amounting to £41,632.

(a)   **What will be the balance on the sales ledger control account?**

£

(b)   **Will the balance you calculated in (a) be a debit balance or a credit balance brought down in the sales ledger control account?**

Debit / Credit

The following balances were in the sales ledger at the end of June.

Sales ledger accounts	£
Strellis Ltd	5,324
Watton plc	11,397
Breem Builders	7,862
Kociejowski & Co	9,356
Patel & Co	4,196
Siddique Retail	4,580

(c)   **Which ONE of the statements below is true?**

	✔
The sales ledger control account balance matches the total of the balances in the sales ledger so no further action is necessary.	
The sales ledger control account balance does not match the total of the balances in the sales ledger so the difference must be investigated.	
It is not important that the balance of the sales ledger control account matches the total of the sales ledger so no further action is necessary.	

This is a summary of transactions with credit customers during the month of July.

(d) **Show whether each entry will be a debit or a credit in the sales ledger control account in the general ledger.**

Sales ledger control

Details	Amount £	Debit ✔	Credit ✔
Sales to credit customers	25,162		
Receipts from credit customers	22,045		
Irrecoverable debts written off	622		
Goods returned by credit customers	1,368		

This is a summary of transactions with credit suppliers during the month of July.

(e) **Show whether each entry will be a debit or a credit in the purchases ledger control account in the general ledger.**

Purchases ledger control

Details	Amount £	Debit ✔	Credit ✔
Discounts received	218		
Goods bought on credit	15,394		
Goods returned to credit suppliers	1,033		
Payments made to credit suppliers	12,176		

2.6   During the last VAT quarter, a VAT payment of £5,247 was made by BACS transfer.

(a)   **What would have been the entries in the general ledger to record this payment?**

Select your entries for the 'Account name' column from the following:

BACS, Bank, Cash, VAT Control

Account name	Amount £	Debit ✔	Credit ✔

At the end of the last VAT quarter, the VAT control account had debit entries amounting to £22,364 and credit entries amounting to £27,406

(b)   **What will be the balance on the VAT control account?**

£

(c)   **Will the balance you calculated in (b) be a debit or a credit balance brought down in the VAT control account?**

Debit / Credit

This is a summary of the VAT transactions during the current VAT quarter.

(d) **Show whether each entry will be a debit or a credit in the VAT control account in the general ledger.**

Summary of VAT transactions

Details	Amount	Debit	Credit
	£	✔	✔
VAT recorded in sales day book	30,324		
VAT recorded in purchases day book	18,386		
VAT recorded in sales returns day book	1,469		
VAT recorded in purchases returns day book	729		
VAT recorded in cash book from cash purchases	1,876		
VAT recorded in cash book from cash sales	3,194		
VAT recorded in petty cash book	26		
Journal to record the VAT amount of an irrecoverable debt written off	321		

2.7 **(a)** Banks offer a variety of services to customers including credit cards, loans and standing orders.

Match each of these four services to the most appropriate description in the table below:

debit card   **personal loan**   **standing order**   **direct debit**

Payment of a bill requiring regular equal payments	
A loan for business use	
A mortgage loan for house purchase	
A loan for buying a new TV	
A cheque used for paying a bill	
Payment of a bill by variable amount payments	
House insurance cover	
A plastic card which takes money from a bank account	
A plastic card which enables you to pay at a later date	

(b) Select THREE services most likely to be offered by the smaller Building Societies from the list below, indicating your answer by ticking the appropriate boxes.

	✔
Business loan	
House mortgage loan	
Payroll services	
Travel money	
Debit cards	
Arranging wills	

2.8 **(a)** Supermarkets nowadays take payments at the till using 'Chip & PIN' cards.

Indicate below whether each statement is either true or false.

	True ✔	False ✔
Payment authorisation or refusal is automatic.		
The PIN number has to be entered by the customer at the till.		
The PIN number has to be confirmed with the till operator.		
If the limit is exceeded authorisation will be refused.		

(b) When paying a credit card bill the whole amount owing must be paid by the due payment date.

Indicate whether this statement is true or false.

True ✔	False ✔

(c)   You work in the Accounts Department at Wyvern Trading Ltd and receive this cheque through the post. Today's date is 31 May 2012.

Examine the details on the cheque and indicate whether the statements that follow are true or false.

SOUTHERN BANK PLC **Milsom Street, Bath**	date **21 May 2012** 83-77-03

Pay   **Wyvern Trading Limited** _____ only

Five hundred and twenty three pounds 50p ——— £ 523.50

Account payee only

AVCO LIMITED

842313   837703   70164033

	True ✔	False ✔
There is no problem – the cheque can be paid into the bank as it is.		
There is no problem – the cheque can be completed by you and paid into the bank.		
There is a problem – the cheque will have to be returned to AVCO Limited.		
There is a problem – AVCO will have to give their telephone authorisation for payment of the cheque.		

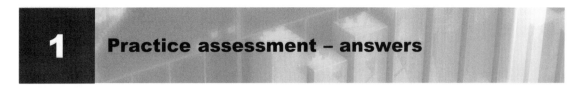

1   Practice assessment – answers

Section 1

Task 1.1

(a)

Account name	Amount £	Debit ✓	Credit ✓
Suspense	12,546	✓	

(b)

Error in the general ledger	Error disclosed by the trial balance ✓	Error NOT disclosed by the trial balance ✓
Discount received of £72 has been recorded in the discount received account as £27	✓	
A bank payment to a credit supplier has been omitted from cash book and purchases ledger control account		✓
Commission received of £150 has been credited to rent received account		✓
Sales returns of £225 have been credited to sales account	✓	
A bank payment for vehicle repairs has been recorded in the cash book only	✓	
The balance of sales account has been calculated incorrectly	✓	

Task 1.2

(a)

Account name	Amount £	Debit ✓	Credit ✓
Bad debts	920	✓	
Value Added Tax	184	✓	
Sales ledger control	1,104		✓

(b)

Account name	Amount £	Debit ✔	Credit ✔
Cash	250	✓	
Bank overdraft	2,359		✓
Vehicles	12,500	✓	
Machinery	8,400	✓	
Capital	25,410		✓
Inventory (stock)	3,987	✓	
Sales ledger control	4,381	✓	
Purchases ledger control	3,326		✓
Rent and rates	1,085	✓	
Miscellaneous expenses	492	✓	
Journal to record the opening entries of the new business			

Task 1.3

(a)

Account name	Amount £	Debit ✓	Credit ✓
Wages expense	40,827	✓	
Wages control	40,827		✓

(b)

Account name	Amount £	Debit ✓	Credit ✓
Wages control	11,480	✓	
HM Revenue and Customs	11,480		✓

(c)

Account name	Amount £	Debit ✓	Credit ✓
Wages control	25,867	✓	
Bank	25,867		✓

(d)

Account name	Amount £	Debit ✓	Credit ✓
Wages control	3,480	✓	
Pension fund	3,480		✓

Task 1.4

(a)   (i)

Account name	Amount £	Debit ✔	Credit ✔
Purchases ledger control	4,760	✔	

(ii)

Account name	Amount £	Debit ✔	Credit ✔
Purchases ledger control	5,760		✔

(iii)

Account name	Amount £	Debit ✔	Credit ✔
Suspense	1,000	✔	

(b)   (i)

Account name	Amount £	Debit ✔	Credit ✔
Bank	220	✔	
Commission received	220		✔

(ii)

Account name	Amount £	Debit ✔	Credit ✔
Bank	220	✔	
Commission received	220		✔

Task 1.5

Rent received

Details	Amount £	Details	Amount £
Rent paid	450		

Rent paid

Details	Amount £	Details	Amount £
		Rent received	450

Purchases

Details	Amount £	Details	Amount £
Suspense	500		

Suspense

Details	Amount £	Details	Amount £
Balance b/f	625	Purchases	500
		Office expenses	125

Office expenses

Details	Amount £	Details	Amount £
Suspense	125		

Task 1.6

Account name	Balances extracted on 30 June £	Balances at 1 July	
		Debit £	Credit £
Vehicles	17,800	17,800	
Inventory (stock)	4,925	4,925	
Sales ledger control	6,318	6,318	
Petty cash control	49	49	
Capital	18,835		18,835
Loan from bank	3,841		3,841
VAT owing to HM Revenue and Customs	1,596		1,596
Purchases ledger control	4,389		4,389
Bank overdraft	1,497		2,057
Sales	86,833		86,833
Sales returns	2,076	2,436	
Purchases	41,783	41,783	
Purchases returns	1,086		1,086
Wages	33,965	33,965	
Advertising	3,864	3,864	
Insurance	1,597	1,597	
Heating and lighting	1,326	1,326	
Rent and rates	2,847	2,847	
Vehicle expenses	1,727	1,727	
Suspense account (credit balance)	200	–	–
Totals		118,637	118,637

Section 2

Task 2.1

(a)   Cash book – credit side

Details	Discount	Cash	Bank	VAT	Payables (creditors)	Cash purchases	Stationery expenses
Balance b/f			3,078				
Gower Ltd		144		24		120	
P Billingham		96		16		80	
McIntyres	25		1,700		1,700		
Bromfield Stationery			192	32			160
Kalsi Ltd			845		845		
Totals	25	240	5,815	72	2,545	200	160

(b)   Cash book – debit side

Details	Discount	Cash	Bank	Receivables (debtors)
Balance b/f		445		
G Brownlow			1,286	1,286
S Barnett	20		565	565
Totals	20	445	1,851	1,851

(c) | £205 |

(d) | £3,964 |

(e)

Debit	
Credit	✓

Task 2.2   **(a) – (c)**

CASH BOOK

Date 20XX	Details	Bank £	Date 20XX	Cheque number	Details	Bank £
01 Jun	Balance b/f	1,487	01 Jun	114117	Hendric & Co	395
04 Jun	Cottle Ltd	4,806	01 Jun	114118	Harrup & Noyes	1,310
20 Jun	W Waugh	2,108	10 Jun	114119	Farr Ltd	2,218
24 Jun	Pardo Ltd	1,746	18 Jun	114120	Bradnock Trading	1,036
24 Jun	Torre & Co	542	18 Jun	114121	Paxtons	1,427
21 Jun	Bayer Ltd	1,095	18 Jun	114122	Filiaps Ltd	798
21 Jun	Allen plc	2,786	20 Jun		Wyvern Council	235
			22 Jun		JA Finance	592
			24 Jun		Bank charges	45
			25 Jun		Balance c/d	6,514
		14,570				14,570
26 Jun	Balance b/d	6,514				

(d)

Bank reconciliation statement as at 25 June 20XX	
Balance as per bank statement	£6,060
Add	
Name: Pardo Ltd	£1,746
Name: Torre & Co	£ 542
Total to add	£2,288
Less	
Name: Bradnock Trading	£1,036
Name: Filiaps Ltd	£ 798
Total to subtract	£1,834
Balance as per cash book	£6,514

Task 2.3

Petty cash book

Debit side		Credit side					
Details	**Amount** £	**Details**	**Amount** £	**VAT** £	**Postage** £	**Travel** £	**Stationery** £
Balance b/f	200.00	Western Trains	22.50			22.50	
		Post office	9.60		9.60		
		Stationery Supplies Ltd	18.72	3.12			15.60
		Balance c/d	149.18				
	200.00		200.00	2.73	9.60	22.50	15.60

Task 2.4

(a)

Petty cash voucher
Date: 04.07.XX
Number: PCV145
Taxi fare from station
Net   £12.00
VAT   £ 2.40
Gross   £14.40

Petty cash voucher
Date: 04.07.XX
Number: PCV146
Printer cartridge for SC printer
Net   £16.40
VAT   £ 3.28
Gross   £19.68

(b)

Amount in petty cash box	£98.90
Balance on petty cash account	£98.20
Difference	£ 0.70

(c)

Petty cash reimbursement	
Date: 31.07.20XX	
Amount required to restore the cash in the petty cash box	£121.30

Task 2.5

(a)

Details	Amount	Debit	Credit
	£	✔	✔
Balance of credit suppliers at 1 June	18,392		✔
Goods bought on credit	6,874		✔
Payments made to credit suppliers	8,937	✔	
Discounts received	154	✔	
Goods returned to credit suppliers	529	✔	

(b)

Cr £15,646	✔

(c)

	£
Balance on purchases ledger control account at 30 June	15,646
Total of the purchases ledger balances at 30 June	16,231
Difference	585

(d)

An invoice was entered twice in the purchases ledger	✔

(e)

Reconciliation of the purchases ledger control account assures managers that the amount showing as outstanding to suppliers is correct.	✔

Task 2.6

(a)

VAT control

Details	Amount £	Details	Amount £
Purchases	9,080	Sales	14,800
Sales returns	368	Purchases returns	248
		Cash sales	376

(b)

Yes	✓
No	

Task 2.7

(a)

Service	Offered by banks ✔	Offered by building societies ✔
Personal current account	✔	✔
Business current account	✔	
House mortgage	✔	✔
Business loan	✔	
Savings account	✔	✔
Safe custody	✔	

(b)

	True	False
Interest may be paid on the amount of the cheque after two working days.	✔	
The amount of the cheque may only be taken out of the bank after four working days.	✔	
The amount of the cheque may only be taken out of the bank after six working days.		✔
The amount of the cheque paid in is only guaranteed and safe to be withdrawn out of the account after six working days.	✔	
The amount of the cheque paid in is only guaranteed and safe to be withdrawn out of the account after ten working days.		✔

(c)   payment without having to issue a cheque, currency withdrawals overseas, payment deducted from the bank account electronically

Task 2.8

(a)   A small value payment for office expenses is often made using **petty cash**, whereas a very large payment, to buy property for example, will be made using the **CHAPS** system. Businesses often use the **BACS** system for making irregular **direct credit** payments to a supplier's bank account, or regular payments for rent by means of a **standing order.**

(b)   Telephone sales   No

Internet sales   No

In a restaurant   Yes

At a supermarket   Yes

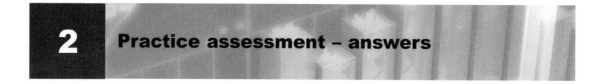

Section 1

Task 1.1

(a)

Account name	Amount £	Debit ✔	Credit ✔
Suspense	19,847	✔	

(b)

Error in the general ledger	Error disclosed by the trial balance	Error NOT disclosed by the trial balance
Recording a bank payment for heat and light on the debit side of both the bank and heat and light account.	✔	
Recording a payment for motor repairs in the motor vehicles account.		✔
Recording a sales credit note on the debit side of the sales ledger control account and the credit side of the sales returns account.		✔
Incorrectly calculating the balance on the rent account.	✔	
Recording a payment by cheque to a creditor in the bank account and purchases ledger only.	✔	
Recording a bank payment of £470 for motor repairs as £4700 in both accounts.		✔

Task 1.2

(a)

Account name	Amount £	Debit ✔	Credit ✔
Bad debts	1,560	✔	
VAT	312	✔	
Sales ledger control	1,872		✔

(b)

Account name	Amount £	Debit ✔	Credit ✔
Cash	150	✔	
Cash at bank	12,350	✔	
Capital	23,456		✔
Fixtures and Fittings	2,100	✔	
Insurance	825	✔	
Loan from bank	10,000		✔
Miscellaneous expenses	218	✔	
Motor vehicle	15,650	✔	
Office expenses	613	✔	
Rent and rates	1,550	✔	
Journal to record the opening entries of new business			

Task 1.3

(a)

Account name	Amount £	Debit ✔	Credit ✔
Wages expense	6,966	✔	
Wages control	6,966		✔

(b)

Account name	Amount £	Debit ✔	Credit ✔
HM Revenue and Customs	3,158		✔
Wages control	3,158	✔	

(c)

Account name	Amount £	Debit ✔	Credit ✔
Bank	3,508		✔
Wages control	3,508	✔	

(d)

Account name	Amount £	Debit ✔	Credit ✔
Trade Union	300		✔
Wages control	300	✔	

Task 1.4

(a)

(i)

Account name	Amount £	Debit ✔	Credit ✔
VAT	1,100		✔

(ii)

Account name	Amount £	Debit ✔	Credit ✔
VAT	1,000	✔	

(iii)

Account name	Amount £	Debit ✔	Credit ✔
Suspense	100	✔	

(b)   Record the journal entries needed in the general ledger to:

(i)

Account name	Amount £	Debit ✔	Credit ✔
Heat and light	350	✔	
Bank	350		✔

(ii)

Account name	Amount £	Debit ✔	Credit ✔
Heat and light	350	✔	
Bank	350		✔

Task 1.5

(a)   **Office stationery**

Details	Amount £	Details	Amount £
Suspense	167		

Rent and rates

Details	Amount £	Details	Amount £
		Suspense	1,800

Suspense

Details	Amount £	Details	Amount £
Rent and rates	1,800	Balance b/f	1,633
		Office stationery	167

Bank interest received

Details	Amount £	Details	Amount £
Bank interest charged	98		

Bank interest charged

Details	Amount £	Details	Amount £
		Bank interest received	98

Task 1.6

	Balances extracted on 30 June	Balances at 1 July	
	£	Debit £	Credit £
Motor vehicles	34,536	34,536	
Fixtures and fittings	17,350	17,350	
Stock	7,300	7,300	
Bank overdraft	5,521	**5,521**	
Petty cash	100	100	
Sales ledger control	100,625	100,625	
Purchases ledger control	56,119		56,119
VAT owing to HM Revenue and Customs	8,300		8,300
Capital	22,844		22,844
Sales	222,955		222,955
Purchases	112,250	112,250	
Purchases returns	6,780		**6,870**
Wages	25,700	25,700	
Motor expenses	1,368	1,368	
Office expenses	3,354	3,354	
Rent and rates	1,444	1,444	
Heat and light	2,155	2,155	
Insurance	3,165	3,165	
Miscellaneous expenses	2,220	2,220	
Suspense account (debit balance)	10,952		
Totals		**317,088**	**317,088**

Section 2

Task 2.1 **(a)** **Cash-book – credit side**

Details	Discount	Cash	Bank	VAT	Creditors	Cash purchases	Motor expenses
Balance b/f			16,942				
B. Smithson Ltd		240		40		200	
H Hamnet		192		32		160	
Renee Reid		320				320	
Tenon Ltd	80		3,600		3,600		
Vernon Motor Repairs			48	8			40
Total	80	752	20,590	80	3,600	680	40

(b)   Cash book – debit side

Details	Discount	Cash	Bank	Debtors
Balance b/f		1,325		
G Brownlow			749	749
S Barnett	30		300	300
Total	30	1,325	1,049	1,049

(c)   £573

(d)   £19,541

(e)   Credit

Task 2.2   (a) to **(c)**

Cash book as at 23 June

Date 20XX	Details	Bank £	Date 20XX	Cheque number	Details	Bank £
01 June	Balance b/f	15,189	01 June	111042	Prime kitchens	10,000
16 June	Britten & Bond	175	01 June	111043	Equipdirect	1,420
20 June	Macklin Ltd	950	01 June	111044	Long and Lane	80
21 June	Randle fitments	300	01 June	111045	BLH Ltd	795
12 June	Cabot and Co	571	02 June	111046	MVR Ltd	652
			02 June	111047	Fairfield Ltd	2,500
			13 June	111048	Makin and King	450
			13 June		LBMC	150
			20 June		Insurance Direct	850
			23 June		Bank charges	88
			23 June		Overdraft fees	30
			23 June		Balance c/d	170
		17,185				17,185
24 June	Balance b/d	170				

(d)   Bank reconciliation statement as at 23 June 20XX

Balance per bank statement	£22
Add:	
Name: Macklin Ltd	£950
Name: Randle Firments	£300
Total to add	£1,250
Less:	
Name: MVR Ltd	£652
Name: Makin and King	£450
Total to subtract	£1,102
Balance as per cash book	£170

Task 2.3

(a) and **(b)**   **Petty cash-book**

Debit side		Credit side					
Details	*Amount* *£*	*Details*	*Amount* *£*	*VAT* *£*	*Postage* *£*	*Travel* *£*	*Stationery* *£*
Balance b/f	150.00	Tom's Taxi	18.00			18.00	
		Post Office	30.00		30.00		
		SMP Stationery	43.20	7.20			36.00
		Balance c/d	58.80				
	150.00		150.00	6.30	30.00	18.00	36.00

Task 2.4

(a)

Petty cash voucher PC187 7.07.XX
5 packs A4 envelopes
Net   £14.00
VAT   £2.80
Gross   £16.80

Petty cash voucher PC188 7.07.XX
Fuel for motor van
Net   £32.00
VAT   £6.40
Gross   £38.40

(b)   Amount in petty cash box   £116.15

Balance on petty cash account   £120.00

Difference   £3.85

(c)   Petty cash reimbursement

Amount required to restore the cash in the petty cash box.   £196.55

Task 2.5

(a)

Details	Amount £	Debit ✔	Credit ✔
Balance of creditors at 1 June	50,530		✔
Goods bought on credit	17,504		✔
Payments made to credit suppliers	20,672	✔	
Discount received	392	✔	
Goods returned to credit suppliers	784	✔	

(b)   Cr £46,186

(c)

	£
Purchases ledger control account balance as at 30 June	46,186
Total of subsidiary (purchases) ledger accounts as at 30 June	45,794
Difference	392

(d)   Goods returned may have been entered in the subsidiary ledger twice

(e)   Reconciliation of the purchases ledger control account assures managers that the amount showing as outstanding to suppliers is correct

Task 2.6

(a)   **VAT control**

Details	Amount £	Details	Amount £
Sales returns	560	Sales	34,400
Purchases	19,600	Cash sales	64
		Purchases returns	1,520

(b)   No

Task 2.7

(a)

Service	Not offered by building societies ✔
Foreign Currency	
Loan	
Overdraft	
Safe custody	✔
Savings account	
Telephone banking	

(b)

	True	False
A bank cheque paid into a building society does not have to pass through the clearing system.		✔
A building society cheque paid into a bank does not have to pass through the clearing system.		✔
A bank cheque has to be passed to the bank of the issuer before the money becomes available.	✔	
A building society cheque has to be passed to the bank of the issuer before the money becomes available.		✔

(c)

	✔
Aged debtor analysis	
Aged creditor analysis	
Bank statements	✔
Credit cards	
Debit cards	
Paying in slip stubs	✔
Remittance advice notes	
Supplier invoices	

Task 2.8

(a)

Checks to be made	Cheque	Telephone credit card payment
Check expiry date		✔
Check issue number		
Check not posted dated	✔	
Check security number		✔
Check words and figures match	✔	
Check card has not been tampered with		

(b)

	True	False
When Kitchen Kuts makes payments to suppliers by credit card, the amount leaves the bank current account immediately.		✔
When Kitchen Kuts makes payments to suppliers by debit card, the amount paid does not affect the bank current account.		✔

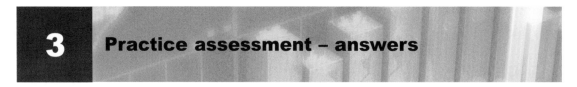

3 Practice assessment – answers

Section 1

Task 1.1

(a)

Account name	Amount £	Debit ✓	Credit ✓
Suspense	1,678		✓

(b)

Description of error	Type of error
Entries have not been made in the general ledger for a transaction.	Error of omission
An entry has been made in the purchases ledger for the correct amount but it has been recorded in the wrong supplier's account.	Error of commission
The cost of fuel for vehicles has been recorded correctly in the general ledger, but the vehicles account has been debited.	Error of principle
Entries in the general ledger have been made in the correct accounts but, instead of £65, the amount has been recorded as £56 in both accounts.	Error of original entry
Entries have been made in the general ledger for a transaction, but on the wrong side of each account.	Reversal of entries
The balance of stationery expenses account has been overstated by £100 and the balance of rent received account has been overstated by £100.	Compensating error

Task 1.2

(a)

Account name	Amount £	Debit ✓	Credit ✓
Irrecoverable debts	1,560	✓	
Value Added Tax	312	✓	
Sales ledger control	1,872		✓

(b)

The Journal

Account name	Amount	Debit	Credit
	£	✔	✔
Bank overdraft	1,524		✔
Capital	15,500		✔
Discount allowed	155	✔	
Heat and light	1,084	✔	
Office equipment	5,450	✔	
Purchases	7,894	✔	
Sales	14,466		✔
Sales ledger control	6,452	✔	
Vehicles	11,500	✔	
VAT owing	1,045		✔
Journal to record the opening entries of the new business			

Task 1.3

(a)   Record the wages expenses

Account name	Amount	Debit	Credit
	£	✔	✔
Wages expense	36,386	✔	
Wages control	36,386		✔

(b)   Record the net wages paid to the employees

Account name	Amount	Debit	Credit
	£	✔	✔
Wages control	24,418	✔	
Bank	24,418		✔

(c) **Record the HM Revenue and Customs liability**

Account name	Amount £	Debit ✓	Credit ✓
Wages control	10,768	✓	
HM Revenue & Customs	10,768		✓

(d) **Record the Pension liability**

Account name	Amount £	Debit ✓	Credit ✓
Wages control	1,200	✓	
Pension	1,200		✓

Task 1.4

(a)

(i) **Remove the incorrect entry**

Account name	Amount £	Debit ✓	Credit ✓
Discounts allowed	110		✓

(ii) **Record the correct entry**

Account name	Amount £	Debit ✓	Credit ✓
Discounts received	110		✓

(iii) **Remove the suspense account balance**

Account name	Amount £	Debit ✓	Credit ✓
Suspense	220	✓	

(b)

(i)   Remove the incorrect entry

Account name	Amount £	Debit ✔	Credit ✔
Office expenses	450	✔	
Bank	450		✔

(ii)   Record the correct entry

Account name	Amount £	Debit ✔	Credit ✔
Office expenses	450	✔	
Bank	450		✔

Task 1.5

Vehicle expenses account

Details	Amount £	Details	Amount £
Miscellaneous expenses	274		

Miscellaneous expenses account

Details	Amount £	Details	Amount £
		Vehicle expenses	274

Office equipment account

Details	Amount £	Details	Amount £
Suspense	2,000		

Suspense account

Details	Amount £	Details	Amount £
Balance b/f	777	Office equipment	2,000
Wages control	1,223		

Wages control account

Details	Amount £	Details	Amount £
		Suspense	1,223

Task 1.6

Trial balance

Account name	Balances extracted on 30 June £	Debit balances at 1 July £	Credit balances at 1 July £
Bank overdraft	3,525		3,525
Capital	15,000		15,000
Commission received	424		642
Discounts received	238		238
Heating and lighting	2,475	2,475	
Irrecoverable debts written off	419	419	
Miscellaneous expenses	1,785	1,785	
Office expenses	1,616	2,341	
Petty cash	250	250	
Purchases	74,630	74,316	
Purchases ledger control	10,721		10,721
Purchases returns	1,047		1,047
Rent paid	3,625	3,625	
Sales	117,618		117,618
Sales ledger control	25,032	25,032	
Sales returns	3,784	3,784	
VAT owing to HM Revenue and Customs	2,419		2,419
Vehicle expenses	5,734	6,048	
Wages and salaries	31,135	31,135	
Totals		**151,210**	**151,210**

Section 2

Task 2.1

(a)

Cash book – credit side

Details	Discount £	Cash £	Bank £	VAT £	Trade Payables £	Cash purchases £	Other expenses £
Balance b/f			5,218				
James Marshall		252		42		210	
Wyvern Council			350				350
Blenheim plc	10		588		588		
K Bialas			720		720		
Total	**10**	**252**	**6,876**	**42**	**1,308**	**210**	**350**

(b)

Cash book – debit side

Details	Discount £	Cash £	Bank £	Trade Receivables £	Other income £
Balance b/f		356			
AGS Supplies			1,345	1,345	
Tyax plc	40		2,312	2,312	
Tom Walton		350			350
Total	**40**	**706**	**3,657**	**3,657**	**350**

(c)   £454

(d)   £–3219

(e)

Account name	Amount	Debit	Credit
Blenheim plc	10		✔

Task 2.2

(a)-(c)

CASH BOOK

Date 20XX	Details	Bank £	Date 20XX	Cheque number	Details	Bank £
04 Jul	Fogg plc	2,314	01 Jul		Balance b/f	1,531
19 Jul	Trader Bills Ltd	854	02 Jul	017630	Bokova Ltd	652
21 Jul	Winton plc	1,716	05 Jul	017631	Palacions Sisters	483
24 Jul	Jamieson Partners	568	15 Jul	017632	Ikpasa plc	1,126
25 Jul	Coopers	2,382	24 Jul	017633	Patel & Sons	210
24 Jul	C & D plc	2,858	20 Jul		TP Ltd	565
			22 Jul		Linton Insurance	420
			24 Jul		Bank charges	126
			25 Jul		Balance c/d	5,579
		10,692				10,692
26 Jul	Balance b/d	5,579				

(d)

Bank reconciliation statement as at 25 July 20XX	
Balance as per bank statement	£ 3,491
Add	
Name: Jamieson Partners	£ 568
Name: Coopers	£ 2,382
Total to add	£ 2,950
Less	
Name: Bokova Ltd	£ 652
Name: Patel & Sons	£ 210
Total to subtract	£ 862
Balance as per cash book	£ 5,579

Task 2.3

(a) & (b)

Petty cash book

Debit side		Credit side					
Details	**Amount** **£**	**Details**	**Amount** **£**	**VAT** **£**	**Postage** **£**	**Travel** **£**	**Stationery** **£**
Balance b/f	150.00	Taxi fare	18.60	3.10		15.50	
		Post office	10.40		10.40		
		Envelopes	16.08	2.68			13.40
		Balance c/d	104.92				
	150.00		150.00	5.78	10.40	15.50	13.40

Task 2.4

(a)

Petty cash reimbursement	
Date: 01.07.20XX	
Amount required to restore the cash in the petty cash box	£ 159.42

(b)

Petty cash voucher
Date: 03.07.20XX Number: PC642
Stationery Net   £20.25 VAT   £ 4.05 Gross   £24.30

(c) £61.43

(d)

Notes and coins	£
1 x £10 notes	10.00
5 x £5 notes	25.00
5 x £2 coins	10.00
9 x £1 coins	9.00
4 x 50p coins	2.00
17 x 20p coins	3.40
12 x 5p coins	0.60
17 x 2p coins	0.34
TOTAL	60.34

(e) £1.09

Task 2.5

(a) £42,715

(b) Debit balance

(c) **The true statement is:**

The sales ledger control account balance matches the total of the balances in the sales ledger so no further action is necessary.

(d)

Sales ledger control

Details	Amount £	Debit ✔	Credit ✔
Sales to credit customers	25,162	✔	
Receipts from credit customers	22,045		✔
Irrecoverable debts written off	622		✔
Goods returned by credit customers	1,368		✔

(e)

Purchases ledger control

Details	Amount	Debit	Credit
	£	✔	✔
Discounts received	218	✔	
Goods bought on credit	15,394		✔
Goods returned to credit suppliers	1,033	✔	
Payments made to credit suppliers	12,176	✔	

2.6

(a)

Account name	Amount	Debit	Credit
	£	✔	✔
VAT control	5,247	✔	
Bank	5,247		✔

(b) £5,042

(c) Credit balance

(d)

Summary of VAT transactions

Details	Amount	Debit	Credit
	£	✔	✔
VAT recorded in sales day book	30,324		✔
VAT recorded in purchases day book	18,386	✔	
VAT recorded in sales returns day book	1,469	✔	
VAT recorded in purchases returns day book	729		✔
VAT recorded in cash book from cash purchases	1,876	✔	
VAT recorded in cash book from cash sales	3,194		✔
VAT recorded in petty cash book	26	✔	
Journal to record the VAT amount of an irrecoverable debt written off	321	✔	

2.7 (a)

Payment of a bill requiring regular equal payments	standing order
A loan for buying a new TV	personal loan
Payment of a bill by variable amount payments	direct debit
A plastic card which takes money from a bank account	debit card

(b)

House mortgage loan	✔
Travel money	✔
Debit cards	✔

2.8 (a)

	True	False
Payment authorisation or refusal is automatic.	✔	
The PIN number has to be entered by the customer at the till.	✔	
The PIN number has to be confirmed with the till operator.		✔
If the limit is exceeded authorisation will be refused	✔	

(b)   False

(c)

	True	False
There is no problem – the cheque can be paid into the bank as it is.		✔
There is no problem – the cheque can be completed by you and paid into the bank.		✔
There is a problem – the cheque will have to be returned to AVCO Limited.	✔	
There is a problem – AVCO will have to give their telephone authorisation for payment of the cheque.		✔